RESTORATION, COLLECTION & COVER EDITOR — **CORY SEDLMEIER**

BOOK DESIGN — **JAY BOWEN** • SVP PRINT, SALES & MARKETING — **DAVID GABRIEL**

EDITOR IN CHIEF — **AXEL ALONSO** • CHIEF CREATIVE OFFICER — **JOE QUESADA**

PUBLISHER — **DAN BUCKLEY** • EXECUTIVE PRODUCER — **ALAN FINE**

SPECIAL THANKS —
MARK BUCKINGHAM, D'ISRAELI, DUNCAN & DIANE FEGREDO, ALLAN HARVEY,
PETER HOGAN, MICHAEL KELLEHER, CHERYL MORGAN, PAUL SHIPLE & ANDREW WOLF

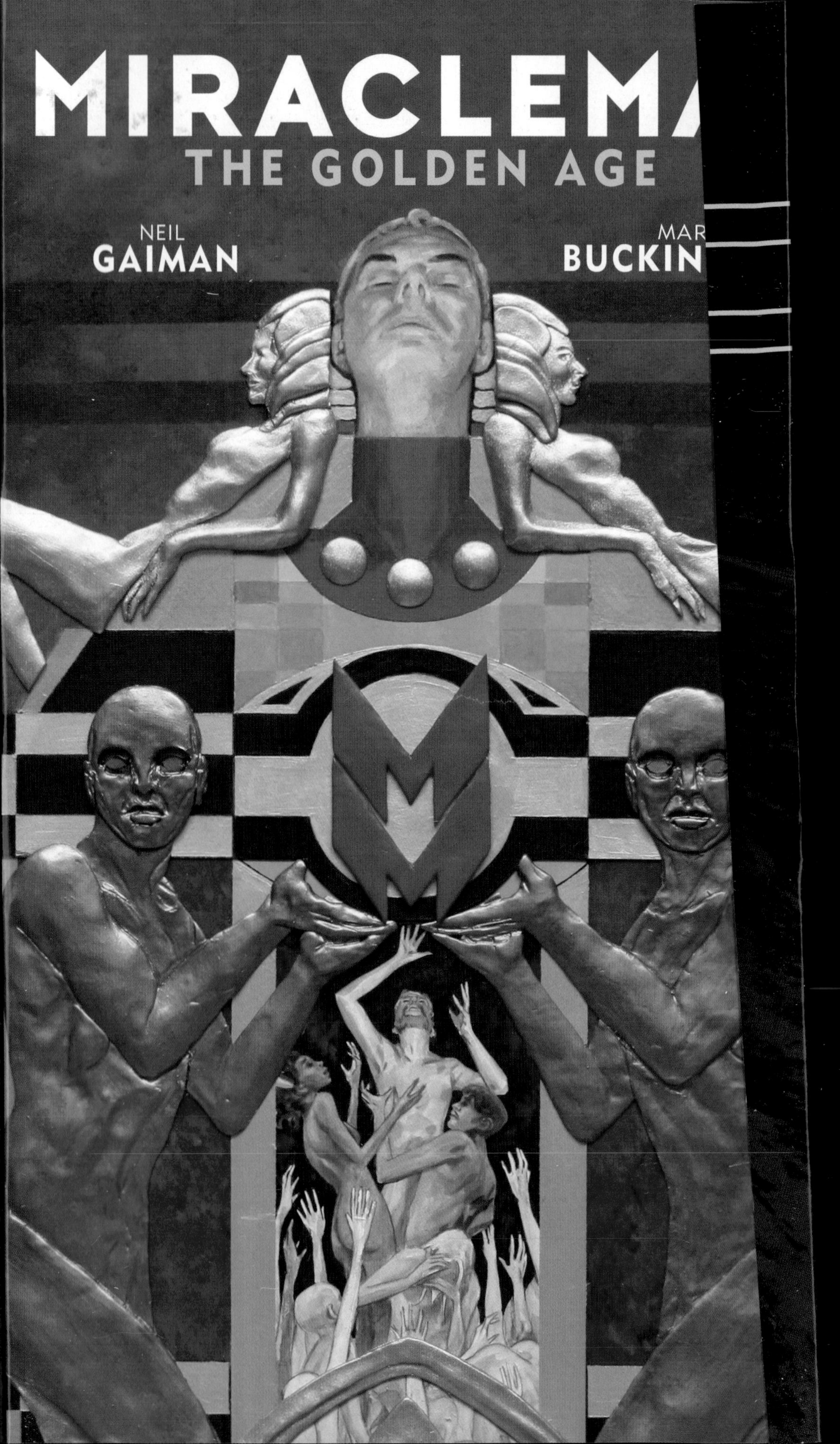
MIRACLEMA
THE GOLDEN AGE
NEIL
GAIMAN
MAR
BUCKIN

MIRACLEMAN

THE
GOLDEN AGE

STORY
NEIL GAIMAN

ART
MARK BUCKINGHAM

COLOR ART
D'ISRAELI

SELECT PAINTED ART (PAGES 47-48, 155-160)
MARK BUCKINGHAM

LETTERING
TODD KLEIN

MIRACLEMAN CREATED BY **MICK ANGLO**

DEDICATIONS

I DON'T KNOW IF YOU CAN DEDICATE A BOOK TO SOMEONE WHO IS 50% RESPONSIBLE FOR CREATING TO IT, BUT I'M DEDICATING THIS BOOK TO MARK BUCKINGHAM ANYWAY. IT'S BEEN THE STRANGEST JOURNEY, OF HIGHS AND LOWS AND ALL SORTS OF UNFORESEEN PROBLEMS AND OCCASIONAL TRIUMPHS. WE'VE WATCHED OUR PUBLISHER GO BANKRUPT, SURVIVED LEGAL NIGHTMARES, AND ARE BRINGING THIS WORK BACK INTO PRINT ALMOST QUARTER OF A CENTURY AFTER IT VANISHED. THANK YOU, BUCKY. YOUR FRIENDSHIP AND CONFIDENCE MADE IT HAPPEN. AND YOU DRAW PRETTY DARNED GOOD TOO.

NEIL GAIMAN

THIS BOOK IS DEDICATED TO NEIL GAIMAN, A TRUE FRIEND AND CONSTANT CHAMPION OF MY WORK, WHO HAS ALWAYS BEEN THERE FOR ME BOTH PROFESSIONALLY AND PERSONALLY. WHEN HE OFFERED ME THE OPPORTUNITY TO JOIN HIM ON *MIRACLEMAN*, BEFORE I EVER HAD A PAGE PUBLISHED IN THE USA, HE TOOK A LEAP OF FAITH I HAVE ALWAYS CHERISHED AND NEVER FORGOTTEN. NEIL HAS ALWAYS ENCOURAGED ME TO EXPERIMENT AND INSPIRES ME TO EXCEL, AND FOR THAT REASON *THE GOLDEN AGE* REMAINS ONE OF THE MOST PRECIOUS MOMENTS IN MY CAREER.

THIS ONE IS ALSO FOR MATT BROOKER, COLOURIST ON *MIRACLEMAN* BOTH IN THE '90S AND AGAIN TODAY, FOR ALL HIS INCREDIBLE WORK AND LOYALTY TO THE SERIES, AND LIFELONG FRIENDSHIP. I MUST ALSO THANK CORY SEDLMEIER FOR HIS DEDICATION TO BRINGING THESE STORIES BACK INTO PRINT, AND TODD KLEIN, FOR HIS EXCEPTIONAL LETTERING SKILLS THAT MAKE THIS PROJECT EVEN MORE SPECIAL. FINALLY, I WOULD ALSO LIKE TO THANK MICHAEL AND MERRILEE, FOR THEIR GENEROSITY AND HELP BEHIND THE SCENES.

MARK BUCKINGHAM

MIRACLEMAN
THE GOLDEN AGE

FROM MAN TO MIRACLE

48, A QYS SPACESHIP CRASHED IN WILTSHIRE, ENGLAND. DR
UNZA USED ITS TECHNOLOGY TO TURN A TRIO OF ORPHANS
HUMANS. BY SPEAKING THEIR KEYWORDS, MICKY MORAN,
LESS AND JOHNNY BATES COULD TRANSFORM INTO THE MIRAC
. GARGUNZA CONTROLLED THEM BY INDUCING A DREAM
THEY SHARED FANTASTIC ADVENTURES AS MIRACLEMAN,
LEMAN AND KID MIRACLEMAN.

63, THE BRITISH GOVERNMENT DEEMED THE MIRACLEME
UNZA'S PROJECT ZARATHUSTRA TOO GREAT A THREAT. GAR
PARAGUAY, CONCEALING HIS COVERT CREATION OF MIRACLEW
OUNG NASTYMAN. AN ATOMIC STRIKE WAS LAUNCHED O
LEMAN FAMILY. YOUNG MIRACLEMAN WAS KILLED. KID MIRAC
ED TO LIVE ON AS A SUPERHUMAN AND WAS CORRUPTED
. MIRACLEMAN REVERTED BACK TO MICKY MORAN AND GR
AGE WITH NO MEMORY OF HIS LIFE AS MIRACLEMAN.

32, MORAN'S MEMORY RETURNED. AS MIRACLEMAN, HE FAT
ERHUMAN CHILD, WINTER, AND UNCOVERED THE TRUTH ABO
GARGUNZA CONSPIRED TO POSSESS WINTER AND WAS KILL
LEMAN. THE QYS RETURNED TO EARTH SEEKING TO EXTERM
CREATED FROM THEIR MISAPPROPRIATED TECHNOLOGY. WI
NCE AS A NEW FORM OF "INTELLIGENT LIFE" STAYED
MIRACLEWOMAN CONVINCED THE QYS AND THEIR ENEMIE
MITHS, TO USE EARTH AS A PLACE FOR DÉTENTE AND THE JO
EIR CULTURES.

"IT WAS THE BEST OF TIMES.

"AND WHAT WAS MIRACULOUS WAS THIS: EVERYBODY KNEW IT.

"THE OLD WORLD HAD BEEN TOO INCOMPETENT AND INCOMPLETE FOR WORDS.

"THE NEW WORLD WAS THE WORLD AS WE'D ALWAYS DREAMED IT COULD BE--A GOLDEN DAWN RISING ON AN AGE OF MIRACLES UNDREAMED OF, EXCEPT, PERHAPS, IN THE MOST ESCAPIST OF FANTASIES.

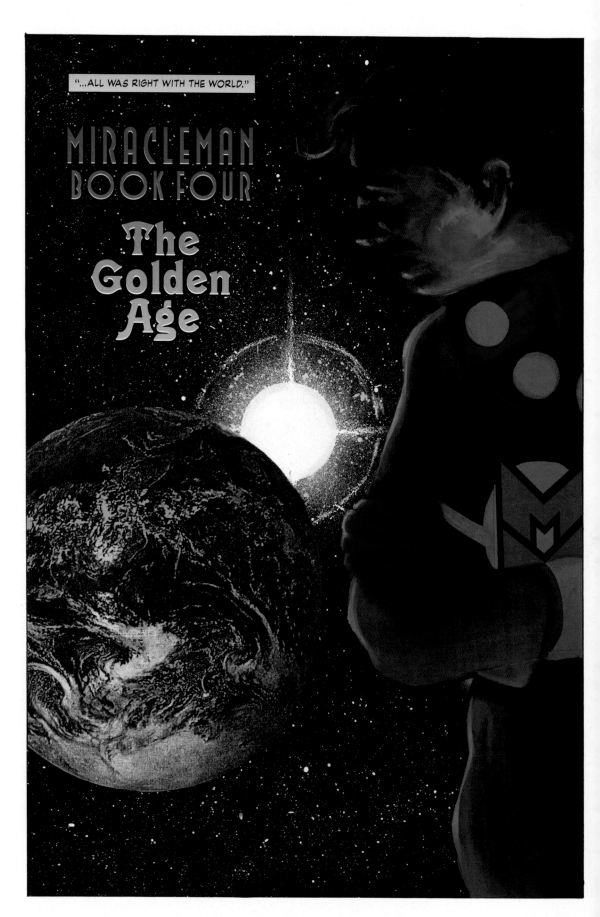

"...ALL WAS RIGHT WITH THE WORLD."

MIRACLEMAN BOOK FOUR

The Golden Age

A PRAYER AND HOPE...

"DATE: AUGUST 3RD, 1987.

"THERE ARE SOME THINGS THAT ARE JUST TOO BIG. YOU CAN'T FIT THEM INTO YOUR HEAD--THEY STOP AT THE EYES AND WON'T GO IN.

"YOU CAN SEE THEM, BUT YOU NEVER BELIEVE THEM, NO MATTER HOW FAMILIAR THEY BECOME.

"YOU THINK ABOUT THEM TOO HARD, YOU MEET YOUR MIND COMING BACK AT YOU.

"GOING UP."

"I MEET MY FELLOW PILGRIMS AT THE BASE CAMP. I HAVE NOTHING TO SAY TO THEM, AND THEY HAVE NOTHING TO SAY TO ME."

"I INTRODUCE MYSELF."

HELLO.

"THERE'S A SICK FEELING IN MY CHEST AS WE WALK TOWARDS THE STEPS, AND MY HEAD BEGINS TO POUND.

"THE HAIRS ON THE BACK OF MY NECK PRICKLE AND RISE.

"WHY?

"FEAR.

"SHEER, STARK TERROR. AND HOPE.

"GOING UP.

"AT EVENING, WE STOP FOR FOOD. WE HAVE BEEN CLIMBING THE CENTRAL STAIRCASE FOR MANY HOURS.

"MY LUNGS ACHE, AS DO MY CALF MUSCLES.

"WE HAVE GONE THROUGH A HALL FILLED WITH WORLD WAR ONE BIPLANES; ANOTHER FILLED WITH MUSICAL INSTRUMENTS.

"THE PLACE WHERE WE STOP CONTAINS NOTHING BUT DINOSAURS. SKELETONS OF STONE AND BONE AND PLASTIC. TINY PLASTIC MODELS AND HUGE ANIMATRONIC RECONSTRUCTIONS.

"BELOW A NEON BRONTOSAURUS WE SIT AND UNWRAP OUR FOOD.

"THE ORIENTAL, TAIPEK, EATS SOMETHING THAT SMELLS SICKLY STRANGE, LIKE ROTTEN HONEY.

"HE OFFERS ME SOME, BUT I REFUSE."

I WONDER WHAT HE'LL BE LIKE.

THE CHILDREN IN MY VILLAGE ARE AFFLICTED BY A DISEASE THAT OUR DOCTORS CANNOT IDENTIFY. THEY ARE WASTING AND DYING. SO THIN AND DRY AND SAD.

I VOLUNTEERED TO COME AND PRAY FOR HIM TO CURE THEM. I *KNOW* HE WILL SAY YES.

WHAT ARE *YOUR* PRAYERS?

"HOPE..."

IT'S LATE. WE'LL SLEEP HERE AND CLIMB AGAIN AT DAWN.

"DURING THE NIGHT I AM WOKEN BY THE SOUNDS OF COPULATION. THE BRONTOSAURUS HAS CEASED TO GLOW, AND IN THE DARKNESS I CANNOT TELL WHO IS DOING WHAT TO WHOM.

"GWEN AND CAIRO?

"GWEN AND TAIPEK?

"TAIPEK AND CAIRO?

"ALL OF THEM?

"FEELING MORE ALONE THAN BEFORE, I WAIT IN SILENCE UNTIL THEY GRUNT AND THRUST THEIR WAY TO EVENTUAL SILENCE, AND, AFTER A WHILE, I DRIFT BACK TO SLEEP.

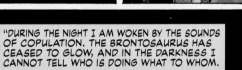

"I DREAM OF CLIMBING STAIRS.

"I ACHE ALL OVER.

"THE RHYTHMS OF THE CLIMB BEGIN TO IMPRINT THEM-SELVES ON MY CONSCIOUSNESS.

"STEP AFTER STEP AFTER STEP, HOUR AFTER HOUR, UNTIL WE REACH THE NEXT FLOOR.

"THEN WE WALK AROUND THE INSIDE OF THIS TOWER OF MIRACLES, THROUGH HALL AFTER HALL FILLED WITH ODDMENTS AND DELIGHTS OF EVERY SHAPE AND KIND, UNTIL WE REACH THE BOTTOM OF THE NEXT RUNG OF STAIRS.

"AND UP.

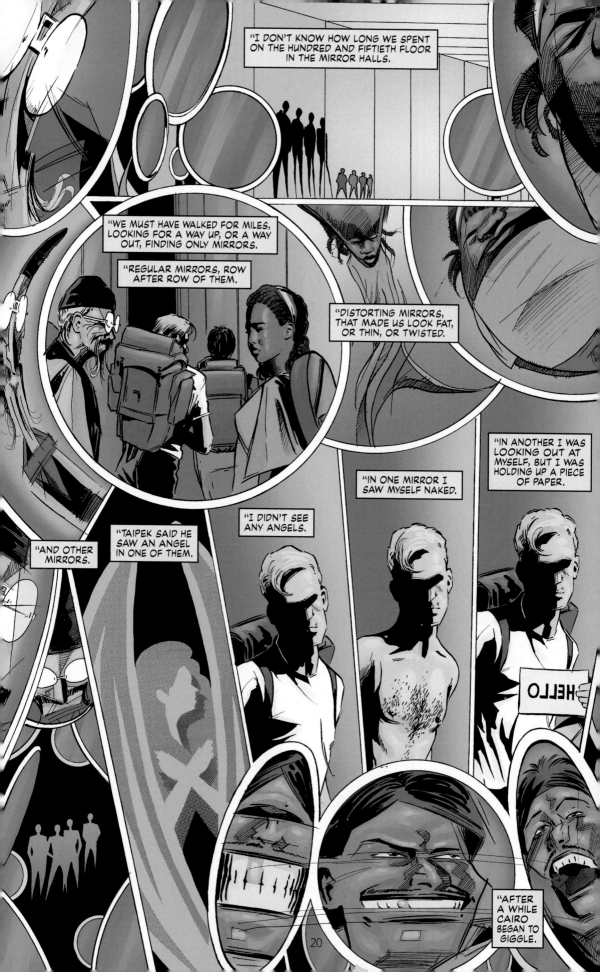

"I TRAINED FOR SIX MONTHS BEFORE COMING HERE, ON QUARRY WALLS, ON TALL BUILDINGS.

"IT'S NOT A HARD CLIMB. DON'T LET ANYONE EVER TELL YOU IT'S A HARD CLIMB. IT'S NOT A HARD CLIMB.

"TO TALK NOW WE NEEDED TO TOUCH HELMETS. I WISHED I COULD HEAR GWEN SINGING.

"WE HAD MADE LOVE ON THE LIBRARY FLOOR, IN THE DARKNESS, BEFORE WE BEGAN TO CLIMB THE OUTSIDE, AND SHE SANG THE WHOLE TIME.

"I WISHED THAT I COULD FLY.

"I WONDERED IF CAIRO THOUGHT HE WAS FLYING, AS HE FELL. IF IT FELT GOOD.

"IF I LET GO, I COULD FIND OUT.

"EASY.

"PERHAPS IN SOME WAY OUR ORDEAL WAS PURIFY- ING US.

"CLEANSING US.

"SANCTIFYING US.

"MAKING US FIT FOR HIS PRESENCE."

29

"THERE ARE SOME THINGS THAT ARE JUST TOO BIG. YOU CAN'T FIT THEM INTO YOUR HEAD--THEY STICK IN THE MIND AND WON'T GO IN...

"YOU NEVER BELIEVE THEM, NO MATTER HOW FAMILIAR THEY BECOME.

"YOU THINK ABOUT THEM TOO HARD, YOU SEE A LITTLE GIRL'S DEAD EYES STARING UP AT YOU.

"HOPE?

"GOING DOWN."

THESE DAYS WE DON'T WORRY ABOUT MUCH.

BATES IS DEAD, AND THE BOMBS HAVE GONE, AND THE AGE OF MIRACLES IS HERE.

MU-UM! I'VE MADE PLANS! ME AND GARRY AND DAVE AND SHARON ARE GOING INTO LONDON THIS WEEKEND! I TOL' YOU! I TOL' YOU AGES AGO!

JASON, I TOLD YOU AGES AGO THAT YOU AND STEPHANIE WERE GOING TO STAY WITH YOUR AUNT MILLIE.

YOU KNOW HOW MUCH SHE WANTS TO SEE YOU...

"STEPHANIE: A YEAR YOUNGER THAN ME AND A PAIN. INTERESTS: DURAN DURAN AND/OR A-HA. HOBBIES: DROPPING ME IN IT.

"AUNT MILLIE: SORT OF LIKE A BATTLESHIP WITH A HANDBAG.

"INTERESTS: HOSPITALS AND PORRIDGE. HOBBIES: TALKING ABOUT HOSPITALS AND FEEDING INNOCENT PEOPLE PORRIDGE."

SHE KEPT MY LATE UNCLE EDWIN'S GALLSTONES IN A JAR ON THE MANTLE-PIECE. HONEST.

FRANKLY, MUM, I'D RATHER DIE IN 'ORRIBLE AGONY!

GARRY WATTS WAS MY BEST FRIEND.

WE'D ALL GO INTO LONDON TOGETHER, HANG AROUND THE WEST END.

SHARON USED TO SHOPLIFT A LOT. SHE WAS DEAD GOOD AT IT. SAID IT WAS A CHALLENGE, LIKE BIG GAME HUNTING. SHE WAS DAVE'S GIRLFRIEND.

"ME AND GARRY WOULD CHECK OUT THE MARKETS, HUNTING FOR GOOD STUFF. BOOTLEG RECORDS. RARITIES.

"GARRY GOT A COPY OF *'THE MAN WHO SOLD THE WORLD'* WITH THE BOWIE-IN-A-DRESS COVER. MUST HAVE BEEN WORTH 100 QUID.

"HE GOT IT FOR THREE POUNDS FIFTY.

"ANYWAY, I GOT SENT TO HAWKING-ON-SEA WITH BLOODY STEPHANIE.

"THE MOST BORING PLACE IN CREATION. I COULD HAVE *SCREAMED.*

"BREAKFAST WAS PORRIDGE. EIGHT O'CLOCK. FROM NINE UNTIL FOUR WE HAD TO BE OUT OF THE HOUSE. WE HAD TO BE BACK BY FOUR, FOR TEA.

"THEY'D ALL BE THERE. I COULD NEVER REMEMBER THEIR NAMES.

"RIPPING INTO THEIR OATMEAL BISCUITS LIKE SEAGULLS PICKING APART A DEAD SEAL.

HASN'T HE GROWN?

DOESN'T HE LOOK LIKE HIS DAD?

YOU REMEMBER ME, LOVE?

DOESN'T HE LOOK LIKE HIS MOTHER?

I NEVER CARED FOR THAT SIDE OF THE FAMILY.

HASN'T HE GROWN?

34

"THEY'D GO **ON** AND **ON** AND **ON** ABOUT WHOEVER WAS IN HOSPITAL THAT WEEK WITH HER LEG OR INSIDES.

"THEY'D MAKE A FUSS OVER STEPHANIE, AND THEY'D IGNORE ME.

"AND STEPHANIE MADE FRIENDS WITH THE GIRL NEXT DOOR, SO THEY'D GO OFF AND TALK ABOUT SIMON LE BON, AND I'D BE LEFT TO ENJOY MYSELF ON THE SEAFRONT.

"YOU COULDN'T **DO** MUCH.

"THERE WAS AN OLD PIER THAT WAS CLOSED OFF. UNDER RECONSTRUCTION.

"IT HAD BEEN UNDER RECONSTRUCTION SINCE 1973.

"THERE WERE HORRIBLE GIFT SHOPS.

"THEY SOLD SWEETS THAT LOOKED LIKE PEBBLES, **KISS-ME-QUICK** HATS, AND STICKS OF ROCK WITH **'HAWKING-ON-SEA'** THROUGH THE MIDDLE.

KISS-ME-QUICK

"THE SKIES WERE GREY AND TIRED, AND THE SEA WAS A MUDDY BROWN, AND THE BEACHES WERE JUST PEBBLES.

"I'D WALK UP AND DOWN THEM, LISTENING TO THE SCREAMS OF THE SEAGULLS AND LOOKING FOR DRIFTGLASS, LIKE IN THE DELANY STORY.

"AND HE'S BEEN STUCK ON THE WEATHER VANE ON THE TOP OF A *CHURCH* WITH HIS *MOUTH* WIDE OPEN.

"AND EVERY TIME THE WIND BLOWS IT GOES THROUGH HIM AND IT SOUNDS LIKE HE'S *SCREAMING*, BUT IT'S JUST THE WIND *RATTLING* THROUGH HIS *VOICEBOX*..."

...*THAT* WAS GARRY.

HE USED TO CALL ME ANNIE, WHEN WE WERE YOUNGER, 'CAUSE OF MY NAME. JASON OAKEY. ANNIE OAKLEY.

"AND *I* WAS TWO HUNDRED MILES AWAY, LISTENING TO THE *SEAGULLS*, THINKING ABOUT WHAT A *GREAT* TIME THEY MUST HAVE BEEN HAVING.

"I POSTED GARRY'S CARD. WHEN I GOT BACK, AUNT MILLIE SAID:

THERE'S BEEN SOME *TROUBLE* IN *LONDON*.

"SHE SAID *SHE* THOUGHT IT WAS THE *RUSSIANS*. THERE WAS A *NEWSFLASH* ON RADIO 2, AND THEN IT WENT *DEAD*.

"THE LOCAL STATIONS WERE STILL BROADCASTING, BUT *THEY* DIDN'T KNOW WHAT WAS GOING ON EITHER.

"I WENT UP TO MY ROOM."

AND I THOUGHT ABOUT THE *FIRST* IMPORTANT THING THAT EVER HAPPENED TO ME.

AFTER LONDON...I THOUGHT OTHER PEOPLE WOULD THINK I'D MADE IT UP..TO BE *IMPORTANT.*

"I WAS NINE OR TEN.

"I HAD THIS PLACE IN EPPING FOREST. IN A HOLLOW TREE. *DON'T* LAUGH. IT WAS MY BOMB SHELTER...

"IN CASE OF NUCLEAR WAR. I HAD HALF A PACKET OF TOFFOS, A PEA SHOOTER, A COPY OF *FIESTA.* SOME FAGS.

"AND I WENT DOWN THERE ONE NIGHT AND I *SAW* HIM. ALL *GLITTERY* AND *SHINY.* AND I SPOKE TO HIM.

I'VE NEVER TOLD *ANYONE* THIS. BEFORE LONDON, I THOUGHT MAYBE I'D *IMAGINED* IT.

"AND I SAID TO HIM, *'PROVE* TO ME YOU'RE A SUPER HERO,' SO HE *WAVES* AT THIS ROCK AND...

"WHOOMF!

"IT EXPLODES.

"AND I--I CAN'T *BELIEVE* I DID THIS-- I ASKED IF *I* COULD BE HIS BOY PARTNER.

"...KID MIRACLEMAN... *CHRIST.*

"AND I SAID, IF THERE *WAS* A NUCLEAR WAR, WOULD HE *SAVE* ME?

"HE SAID *NO.* MAYBE HE *KNEW* WHAT WAS GOING TO HAPPEN.

"HE SAID, NO PROMISES, BUT HE'D *TRY.* IF HE *COULD.* AND WE SHAKE HANDS AND HE FLIES OFF INTO THE SKY."

JUNE 1990.

IF YOU GO DOWN CACKLE LANE TOWARD FAIRWARP YOU'LL SEE MY WINDMILL ON THE LEFT, PAST THE FORD, WHERE THE RIVER SPILLS OVER THE ROAD.

YOU CAN'T GET HERE BY CAR.

YOU HAVE TO LEAVE YOUR CAR AT THE BOTTOM, THEN WALK UP THE HILL.

IT'S A LONG WALK, I'M AFRAID.

IT'S BEEN HERE FOR YEARS, NOW. SINCE IT WAS AN HISTORICAL MONUMENT. LONG BEFORE IT WAS WORKING.

IT'S THE OLDEST ONE IN THIS PART OF THE COUNTRY. ONCE UPON A TIME (THAT'S A GOOD WAY TO START A STORY, ISN'T IT? *ONCE UPON A TIME*) IT GROUND LOCAL WHEAT INTO FLOUR; NOW IT PULLS POWER FROM THE WIND, PART OF A NETWORK COVERING THE COUNTRY, COVERING THE WORLD.

THE CENTRE BEAM IS OAK--THE ONLY PART OF THE ORIGINAL WINDMILL LEFT. IT MUST HAVE BEEN FELLED OVER THREE HUNDRED YEARS AGO. IT WOULD HAVE BEEN AN ACORN WHEN THE SCRUB AND HEATH THEY CALL THE FOREST WERE TRULY PART OF A FOREST.

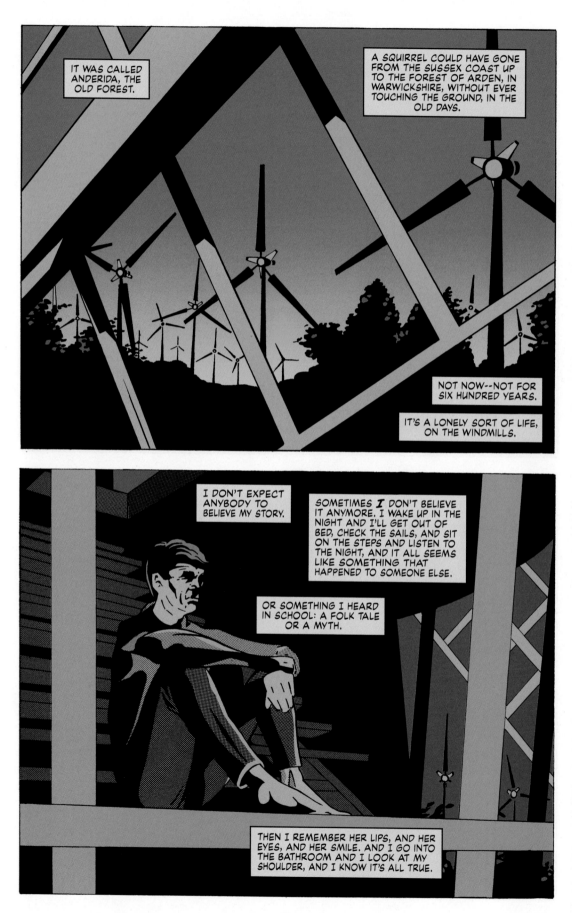

42

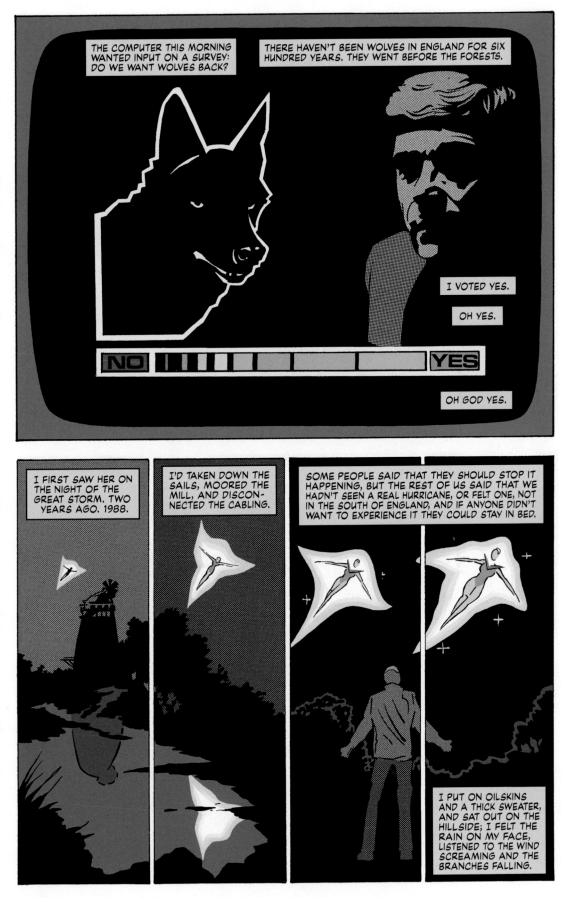

THE COMPUTER THIS MORNING WANTED INPUT ON A SURVEY: DO WE WANT WOLVES BACK?

THERE HAVEN'T BEEN WOLVES IN ENGLAND FOR SIX HUNDRED YEARS. THEY WENT BEFORE THE FORESTS.

I VOTED YES.

OH YES.

NO | | | | | | | | | | | YES

OH GOD YES.

I FIRST SAW HER ON THE NIGHT OF THE GREAT STORM. TWO YEARS AGO. 1988.

I'D TAKEN DOWN THE SAILS, MOORED THE MILL, AND DISCONNECTED THE CABLING.

SOME PEOPLE SAID THAT THEY SHOULD STOP IT HAPPENING, BUT THE REST OF US SAID THAT WE HADN'T SEEN A REAL HURRICANE, OR FELT ONE, NOT IN THE SOUTH OF ENGLAND, AND IF ANYONE DIDN'T WANT TO EXPERIENCE IT THEY COULD STAY IN BED.

I PUT ON OILSKINS AND A THICK SWEATER, AND SAT OUT ON THE HILLSIDE; I FELT THE RAIN ON MY FACE, LISTENED TO THE WIND SCREAMING AND THE BRANCHES FALLING.

44

SHE LIT NO CANDLES.

SHE PEELED HER COSTUME FROM HER BODY. IT LAY ON THE FLOOR LIKE A LIVING THING, WATCHING US.

HER BODY LIT THE ROOM.

SHE TOOK ME, THERE IN THE WOOD, IN THE MILL, WHILE THE WIND AND THE THUNDER ROARED AND RIPPED THROUGH THE DARKNESS OUTSIDE. UNDRESSED ME GENTLY, CAREFULLY, WITH FINGERS THAT COULD HAVE CRUSHED COAL INTO DIAMONDS, KISSED AND CARESSED ME WITH LIPS THAT COULD SUCK THE HEART FROM A STAR.

I HAD NOT BEEN WITH A WOMAN IN FIVE YEARS.

SHE WAS DIFFERENT TO ALL OF THEM.

SHE WAS PERFECT.

IT WAS PERFECT.

WILL I SEE YOU AGAIN?

DO YOU NEED TO?

YES.

PERHAPS.

WHEN IT WAS OVER SHE STAYED BESIDE ME, GENTLY CARESSING ME, WHILE I STARED AT THE PERFECTION OF HER SKIN, OF HER EYES, OF HER HAIR. THEN SHE DRESSED, AND I WALKED HER OUTSIDE, INTO THE DREGS OF THE STORM.

I SPENT THE NEXT WEEK OR SO LOST IN A DREAMWORLD OF MY OWN DEVISING. ON THE OUTSIDE, I WAS REPAIRING MILLS--A FEW HAD BEEN DAMAGED BY THE STORM, ALTHOUGH LESS THAN I HAD FEARED.

INSIDE, I WAS IMAGINING:

CHALLENGING HIM. PUNCHING HIM THROUGH A BUILDING.

(NO.)

WHAT IS IT YOU'RE AFRAID OF?

WHAT DO YOU MEAN?

WHY DID YOU LEAVE ANITA?

YOU KNOW ABOUT THAT?

I KNOW ABOUT ALL OF THEM. ANITA. MELISSA. CAROLYN.

WHO?

SHE HAD A BASEMENT FLAT NEAR PICCADILLY CIRCUS. DON'T YOU REMEMBER?

I REMEMBERED. CAROLYN HAD PERFECT, MODEL LOOKS: BUT THE FLAT WAS SQUALID AND STANK OF ROTTEN ORANGES. AND WHEN WE GOT INTO BED, I DISCOVERED AN APPENDIX SCAR SNAKING ACROSS HER LOWER ABDOMEN, THE FLESH PUCKERED AND WHITE. HER BEAUTY WAS IRRETRIEVABLY FLAWED.

THE NEXT DAY, I RESIGNED FROM MY JOB IN THE GALLERY AND CAME DOWN HERE.

STRANGE. I HAD FORGOTTEN HER NAME.

55

THE TIME OF MYTHS IS RETURNING: STORIES THAT SHAPE THE WORLD, AS THE WORLD ITSELF IS BEING RESHAPED BY THE NEW GODS THAT REIGN IN HIGH OLYMPUS.

WHERE MY LIFE OVERLAPPED WITH HERS, IT HAS BECOME MYTH, AND IT HAS REDEEMED ME.

I AM PLACING MY STORY ON THE 'NET; POTENTIALLY IT COULD BE READ BY ANYONE IN THE WORLD.

I HOPE YOU LEARN FROM IT, YOU WHO WILL READ THIS, WHETHER IN ENGLISH, OR LITHUANIAN, OR TAGALOG, OR MALAY...

I HOPE YOU LIKE IT.

IF YOU WANT, I WILL TELL YOU MY STORY IN PERSON.

I'M AVAILABLE. I'LL SHOW YOU AROUND THE WINDMILL, IF YOU WISH.

GO DOWN CACKLE LANE TOWARD FAIRWARP. YOU'LL SEE IT ON THE LEFT, PAST THE FORD, WHERE THE RIVER SPILLS UP OVER THE ROAD WHENEVER IT RAINS.

58

THEY SAID ON "NEWSROUND" THAT THAT SORT OF THING'S GOIN' TO BE HAPPENIN' MORE AND MORE.

BAGS I GET BITTEN BY THE RADIOACTIVE SPIDER.

DON'T BE A *PRAT*, JASON. IF YOU GOT BITTEN BY A RADIOACTIVE SPIDER YOU'D *DIE*.

IN THE OLD DAYS, MAYBE. BACK WHEN THINGS WAS BORING, NOT ANY MORE.

HE'S *RIGHT.* SORT OF, ANYWAY.

OH, DON'T *YOU* START, JACKS.

THE PROBABILITIES ARE CHANGING.

HUH?

WE DID IT LAST WEEK, IN RELIGIOUS STUDIES. IT WOULD BE A MIRACLE IF YOU GAINED POWERS FROM SOMETHING LIKE THAT.

IT'S *NOT* IMPOSSIBLE, BECAUSE ON A QUANTUM LEVEL, *NOTHING'S* IMPOSSIBLE. IT'S JUST VERY, VERY *UNLIKELY*-- TO THE POINT OF VIRTUAL IMPOSSIBILITY.

BUT MIRACLES ARE HAPPENING MORE AND MORE NOW. PIGGSY SAID THAT IT'S SOMETHING TO DO WITH DEFORMING PROBABILITIES.

ONE IMPOSSIBLE THING MAKES OTHER IMPOSSIBLE THINGS HAPPEN.

PIGGSY'S FULL OF SHIT.

AN' HE PICKS HIS NOSE. I SEEN HIM DO IT.

WELL, ANYWAY, THAT'S WHAT HE SAID.

I REMEMBER WHEN ONE OF US WAS ALLOWED UP TO THE CAPSTONE, FOR A PARTY. HE DROPPED NAMES CASUALLY FOR MONTHS. MIRACLEMAN. MIRACLEWOMAN. WINTER.

WE JUST IGNORED HIM.

IT COULD HAVE BEEN ANY OF US.

UH. MORS?

YES.

BORGHELM

warhol

I'VE GOT A LITTLE PRESENT FOR YOU. IT'S NOTHING SPECIAL. I THOUGHT MAYBE YOU'D LIKE IT. I *MADE* IT.

BORGHELM

warhol

THANK YOU, ANDEK.

IT'S BEEN A LONG TIME SINCE I'VE BEEN HERE. NOT SINCE HE BROUGHT ME BACK.

I'M RESTORING A NEW GUEST, ANDEK.

I WISH YOU TO BE HIS *FRIEND*. YOU MAY ANSWER HIS QUESTIONS. HELP HIM TO *ACCLIMATISE*.

FINE.

66

THE SIXTH ANDY WARHOL.

YES. IT WAS MY. UH, TURN.

...WHERE *IS* THIS PLACE?

WE'RE IN THE BASEMENT OF A BIG, UH, PYRAMID THAT COVERS MOST OF, UH.

LONDON.

MIRACLEMAN. *HE* DID THIS. HE *KILLED* ME. THEN HE DID THIS. AND NOW HE'S BROUGHT ME *BACK.*

MM. UH, *MORS* REALLY BROUGHT YOU BACK. THERE WAS AN, UM, THEY WENT TO THE JUNGLE. SOMEWHERE. AND THEY BROUGHT BACK YOUR HIP. IT WAS ALL THAT WAS *LEFT.*

AND THEY GREW ME FROM THAT. I *SEE.* A CLONAL BODY...

NO. YOU-- YOU AREN'T A CLONE. THE BODY'S A *MACHINE.* THEY NEED *CELLS* FOR THE *MEMORY.*

HMM. SO DOES THAT MEAN THAT MEMORY IS HOLOGRAPHIC? THAT EACH CELL CONTAINS THE ENTIRETY? OBVIOUSLY NOT? MAGNETIC FIELDS, PERHAPS. OR KIRLIAN FIELDS...

I DON'T KNOW THAT STUFF.

YES.

ANDY WARHOL? THE *ARTIST?*

I LIKED SOME OF YOUR WORK. THERE WAS A *FLATNESS* TO IT THAT APPEALED TO ME.

UM. THANK YOU.

SO, WHAT NOW?

AM I *FORBIDDEN* TO EXPLORE THIS BRAVE NEW WORLD?

UH HUH. BUT I'LL COME AND SEE YOU EVERY DAY. IF YOU WANT.

AND, UH, MAYBE MORS WILL LET YOU OUT IN A BIT. THERE'S SOME KIND OF ELECTRIC FIELD THAT KEEPS YOU ALIVE.

MOST OF THE DEAD PEOPLE CAN GO *ANYWHERE* IN MORS' UNDERGROUND. BUT FOR YOU, IT'S JUST *THIS* PLACE.

I'M *SORRY.*

I *SEE.* GOODBYE, ANDY.

GOODBYE, MISTER GARGUNZA.

68

JUNE 10TH, 1993.

I GO TO SEE HIM EVERY DAY.

THE T-SHIRTS ARE PROVING EXTREMELY POPULAR.

I WISH THERE WAS MONEY DOWN HERE, THOUGH. WITHOUT MONEY, HOW DO YOU KNOW HOW WELL YOU'RE DOING?

IT COULD ALL BE TAKEN AWAY FROM YOU AT ANY MOMENT.

THEY SOLD MY WHOLE COLLECTION AFTER I DIED. I WISH I HAD IT NOW. BUT THE OTHER SEVENTEEN WOULD ONLY BITCH ABOUT IT, AND WE'D ARGUE, AND NUMBER ONE WOULD SAY THAT THE REST OF US WERE HIS IDEA, AND WE'D JUST ARGUE SOME MORE.

EMIL IS WRITING A BOOK.

MY NAME IS EMIL GARGUNZA; ALTHOUGH I AM NOT *ENTIRELY* COGNATE WITH THE PREVIOUS INDIVIDUAL WHO HELD THAT NAME, WHOSE MEMORIES (INASFAR AS I CAN ASCERTAIN) I SHARE.

HIS MEMORIES AND MINE ARE QUALITATIVELY DIFFERENT.

HIS ARE BLURRED, IMPRECISE. SOME OF THEM ARE UNDOUBTEDLY EDITED, CENSORED, FIXED. OTHERS ARE, QUITE SIMPLY, *FORGOTTEN.* I RECALL THE GIST OF EVENTS, LOSING THE EXACT WORDS SAID.

SINCE I HAVE BEEN DEAD I HAVE REMEMBERED *EVERYTHING.*

EACH WORD, EACH VISION, IS EIDETICALLY ETCHED INTO MY MIND, HELD IN CRYSTAL LATTICES AND SUPERCONDUCTORS.

HMM. NOTE TO MYSELF: DO A PAGE OR SO HERE ON MORS, THE QYS. WHEN I KNOW MORE ABOUT HIM. *IT.* THEN CONTINUE...

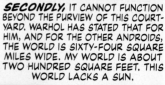

IT IS, IN MANY WAYS, THE FAULT OF HIS RACE THAT I LIVED THE LIFE I DID, AND *DIED* IN THE MANNER OF MY *DEATH.*

IT IS *ALSO* HIS RESPONSIBILITY THAT I LIVE, IN A PERFECT BODY. IT COULD LIVE FOREVER, UNDERNEATH OLYMPUS.

IT HAS, HOWEVER, CERTAIN IMPERFECTIONS. *FIRSTLY,* IT IS, PHYSICALLY, EVERY BIT AS UNPREPOSSESSING AS MY PREVIOUS BODY.

SECONDLY, IT CANNOT FUNCTION BEYOND THE PURVIEW OF THIS COURTYARD. WARHOL HAS STATED THAT FOR HIM, AND FOR THE OTHER ANDROIDS, THE WORLD IS SIXTY-FOUR SQUARE MILES WIDE. MY WORLD IS ABOUT TWO HUNDRED SQUARE FEET. THIS WORLD LACKS A SUN.

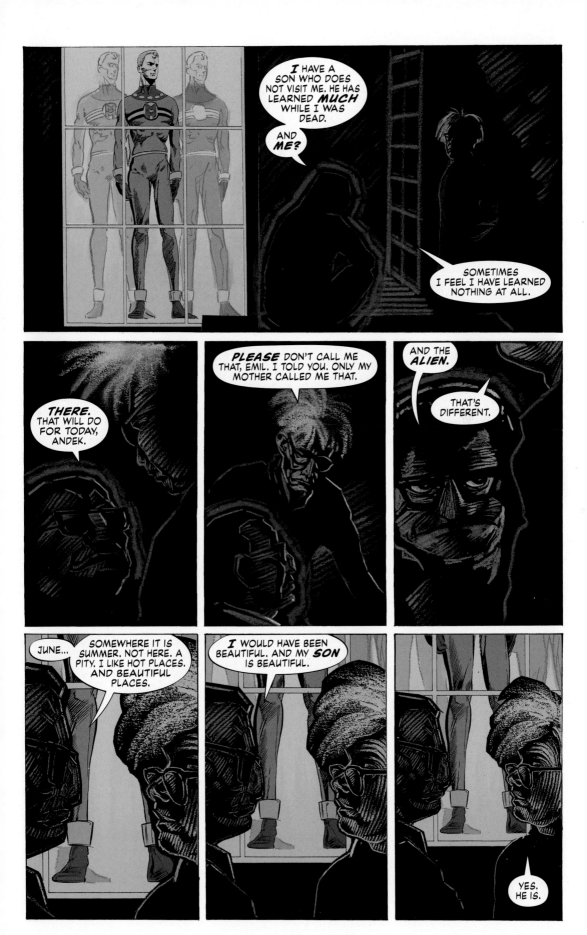

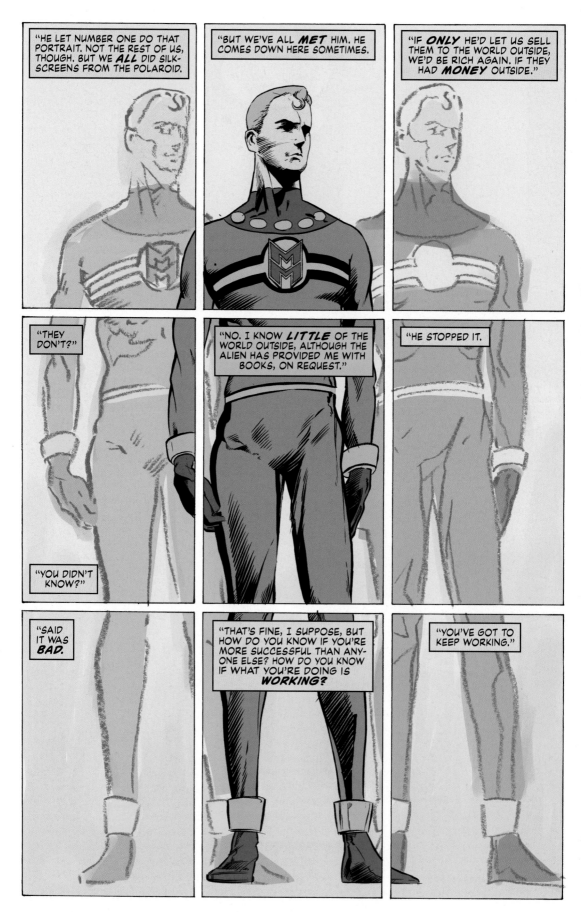

"HE LET NUMBER ONE DO THAT PORTRAIT. NOT THE REST OF US, THOUGH. BUT WE *ALL* DID SILK-SCREENS FROM THE POLAROID.

"BUT WE'VE ALL *MET* HIM. HE COMES DOWN HERE SOMETIMES.

"IF *ONLY* HE'D LET US SELL THEM TO THE WORLD OUTSIDE, WE'D BE RICH AGAIN. IF THEY HAD *MONEY* OUTSIDE."

"THEY DON'T?"

"NO. I KNOW *LITTLE* OF THE WORLD OUTSIDE, ALTHOUGH THE ALIEN HAS PROVIDED ME WITH BOOKS, ON REQUEST."

"HE STOPPED IT.

"YOU DIDN'T KNOW?"

"SAID IT WAS *BAD.*

"THAT'S FINE, I SUPPOSE, BUT HOW DO YOU KNOW IF YOU'RE MORE SUCCESSFUL THAN ANY-ONE ELSE? HOW DO YOU KNOW IF WHAT YOU'RE DOING IS *WORKING?*

"YOU'VE GOT TO KEEP WORKING."

JULY 16TH, 1993.

WE WERE JUST SITTING, TALKING. YOU KNOW, THE WAY YOU DO. EMIL WAS BITCHING ABOUT HOW HE WASN'T ALLOWED TO GO OUT. NOT EVEN INTO THE GARDEN OF THE DEAD, LET ALONE INTO THE WORLD OUTSIDE.

HE WAS ASKING QUESTIONS ABOUT THE GODS. ABOUT HOW ANDY NUMBER ONE WAS ABLE TO PARTY UPSTAIRS, IF THE FIELD THAT KEEPS US GOING ONLY WORKS DOWN HERE.

I DIDN'T KNOW, AND I TOLD HIM.

AND THEN, SHE WAS THERE.

NOW, I SUPPOSE I SHOULD SAY I'M PRETTY BLASÉ. I MEAN, HANGING OUT IN HADES WITH EMIL GARGUNZA, THE FATHER OF THE AGE, WELL, I MEAN, *THAT'S* A NAME TO DROP.

BUT HE'S KIND OF SHORT AND UGLY, AND HE SAYS STUFF I JUST DON'T UNDERSTAND, SO I DON'T SAY ANYTHING, AND HE JUST CARRIES ON LECTURING, AND I JUST WATCH HIM, EVEN THOUGH I DON'T GET IT.

AND WE HAVE A LOT IN COMMON.

SOMETIMES IT FEELS LIKE I HAVE MORE IN COMMON WITH EMIL THAN I DO WITH THE OTHER WARHOLS.

WE WERE TALKING ABOUT OUR BODIES.

MY BODY APPEARS TO BE MADE OF FLESH, FOR ALL INTENTS AND PURPOSES. *HOWEVER,* WHEN I ATTEMPTED TO CUT MY THIGH WITH A KNIFE, EXPERIMENTALLY, I FOUND IT IMPENETRABLE.

AND MY *EYES,* ALTHOUGH WET, ARE OF SOMETHING RESEMBLING PLASTIC. *WHY* THEN ARE THEY MYOPIC? I STILL NEED SPECTACLES? *WHY* HAS THIS NOT BEEN *CORRECTED?*

AND WHY AM I *STILL* SO...

UGLY?

IF YOU WILL. *YES.* WHY AM I STILL UGLY?

I WONDER THE SAME THING ABOUT MYSELF. US. WARHOLS. I *LIKE* PRETTY THINGS. I'D LIKE TO BE PRETTY. BUT THEY MADE ME LIKE I WAS. STUPID NOSE. WEAK CHIN. BAD SKIN. I'VE EVEN GOT SCARS ON MY CHEST.

BUT I DON'T EVER *HURT.* NOT ANYMORE.

AND THEN I SAW THE LIGHT, FLICKERING TOWARD US.

I WAS SO IMPRESSED.

I WONDER IF SHE'D LET ME DO HER PORTRAIT.

IT WAS REALLY HER.

OH *NO*, GRANDFATHER. YOU NEVER DID *ANYTHING* TO ME. I WOULD HAVE KNOWN. YOUR PLANS FOR *ME* NEVER SAW FRUITION. STILL...

...I WONDER WHAT IT WOULD BE LIKE TO HAVE YOU LIVING IN MY HEAD...I DOUBT I'D LIKE IT VERY MUCH. BUT YOU'RE *VERY* CLEVER, YOU KNOW. EVEN THE *QYS* WERE ASTONISHED AT WHAT YOU'D DONE WITH THEIR TECHNOLOGY.

IT WAS AS IF A *MONKEY* HAD GOTTEN HOLD OF A *WALKMAN*, EXTRAPOLATED BACK TO FIRST PRINCIPLES, AND BUILT A *RECORDING STUDIO*. QUITE *INCREDIBLE*.

THANK YOU.

NO PROBLEM. I *ALSO* CAME TO THANK YOU.

WHAT FOR?

FOR *ME*. THANK YOU, GRANDFATHER.

HELLO. I LIKED YOUR EMPIRE STATE BUILDING FILM.

OH. THAT'S NICE.

YES. I LOVE FANTASY.

SHE'S REALLY KEEN. I WISH I COULD INTERVIEW HER. I LIKE THE WAY SHE MOVES.

I REMEMBER THE EMPIRE STATE BUILDING MOVIE. IT WAS OKAY. BUT I DIDN'T REALLY KNOW HOW TO WORK THE CAMERA. IT'S A NEAT BUILDING. MY FATHER WAS IN CONSTRUCTION.

HE NEVER LIKED ME. NOT REALLY.

I LIKE IT WHEN THEY LIKE MY STUFF.

I LIKE IT WHEN THEY PAY ME FOR IT.

"I *REMEMBER* AN INITIAL LIFTING SENSATION AS HE DRAGGED ME UPWARD, FOLLOWED IMMEDIATELY BY A STILLNESS.

"WE WERE AT REST, TOGETHER, AS THE EARTH FELL AWAY, AND THE NIGHT DARKENED TO *BLACK.*

"I HATE TO IMAGINE HOW *FAST* THAT MUST HAVE HAPPENED.

"I WAS NOT HOLDING MY BREATH, AND I HAD NOT YET BEGUN TO BREATH VACUUM, AS HE LOOKED AT ME.

"I HAVE HAD A WHILE SINCE TO CONSIDER THE MEANING OF THAT FINAL LOOK. *THEN,* HOWEVER, TIME FOR REFLECTION WAS DENIED ME.

"HE KISSED ME, AND HE BADE ME GOODBYE, AND HE THREW ME AT THE EARTH.

"I *DIED.*

"THERE WAS NO AIR, BUT I COULD LIP-READ. HE SAID, *'GOODBYE, FATHER.'*

"HE UNDERSTOOD, YOU SEE.

"HE *HAD* TO KILL ME BECAUSE GODS *MUST* KILL THEIR FATHERS. BUT AT THE *END...*

"AT THE *END,* I KNEW HE *LOVED* ME."

TO **GOD?**

SURE. MIRACLEMAN WON'T BE HERE FOREVER. GOD CAN WAIT.

AND MY **PERSONAL** FAVORITES, THE **MORANISTS.**

I DON'T **KNOW** ABOUT THE SOUL, ANDY. BUT I AM **FASCINATED** BY THE HOST OF RELIGIONS THAT ARE SPRINGING UP IN THE WORLD ABOVE.

THE TRANS-TIME INTEGRATIONISTS. THE WITNESSES OF THE CONSPIRACY. THE RATIONAL BRETHREN. THE DEICIDES. THE ANGLOMORES.

I HAVEN'T HEARD OF THEM.

"THEY SUGGEST THAT THE REASON MICHAEL MORAN SUFFERED FROM MIGRAINE HEADACHES WAS INTRA-CRANIAL PRESSURE FROM A **BRAIN TUMOR.**"

UH? SORRY PAUL... I WASN'T LISTENING...

LA LAKELA OR H-

HEY... IS MAN'S SICK! E NEEDS SOME AIR!

HE'S RIGHT, STEVE. HIS GUY LOOKS LIKE HE'S GONNA DIE. WE BETTER GET HIM OUTSIDE...

"THAT IN 1982 IN OXFORD, IN A NUCLEAR POWER STATION, THE TUMOR **HEMORRHAGED.**"

"THEY TEACH THAT MORAN IS **DYING,** THAT IN THE LAST FEW DAYS OF HIS LIFE HIS EXPIRING MIND IS CREATING AN **IMMENSE WISH-FULFILLING FANTASY.**"

"THAT **WE** ARE NOTHING MORE THAN SPARKING NEURONS IN A DYING MAN'S CANCER-RIDDEN **BRAIN.**"

...AND YOU **BELIEVE** THIS?

NO, I BELIEVE THAT **THIS** IS THE REALITY. BUT I PRIZE THE MORANISTS ABOVE ALL OTHERS.

HUMANITY DENIES THE TRUTH IN SO MANY **WONDER-FUL** WAYS.

SEPTEMBER 3RD, 1993.

MORS STOPPED ME THIS EVENING. HALF A DOZEN OF US WERE DOWN AT THE ALABASTER JETTIES, WATCHING THE JOHN BELUSHI CONCERT.

IT WAS FINE.

DIVINE WAS THERE, WITH GLEN. THOSE TWO ARE INSEPARABLE THESE DAYS, BUT I DON'T KNOW WHAT SHE SEES IN HIM. HE'S SO DUMPY AND BORING.

DALI TURNED UP NEAR THE END, ON HIS STUPID GIRAFFE. HE SHOUTED SOMETHING, BUT I DIDN'T UNDERSTAND HIM.

BELUSHI MADE A COUPLE OF JOKES ABOUT US. HE SAID THINGS THAT WEREN'T NICE.

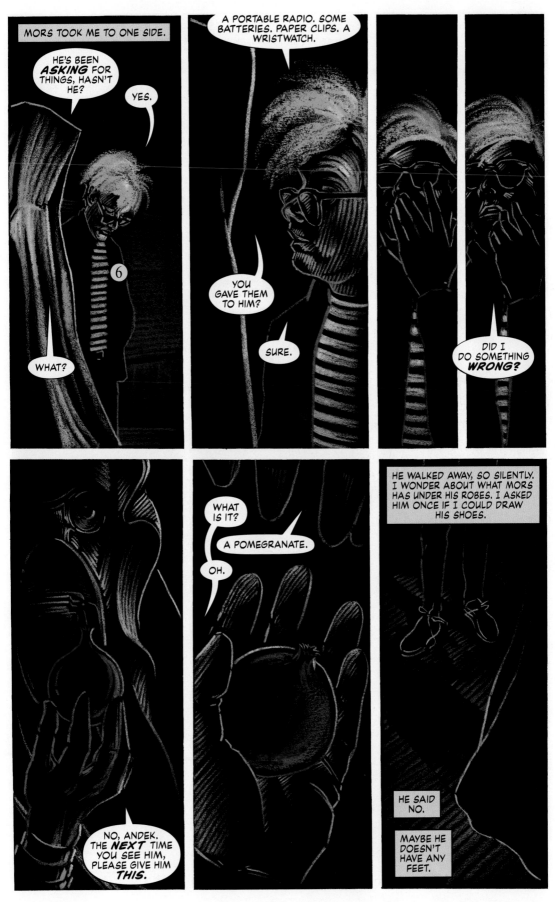

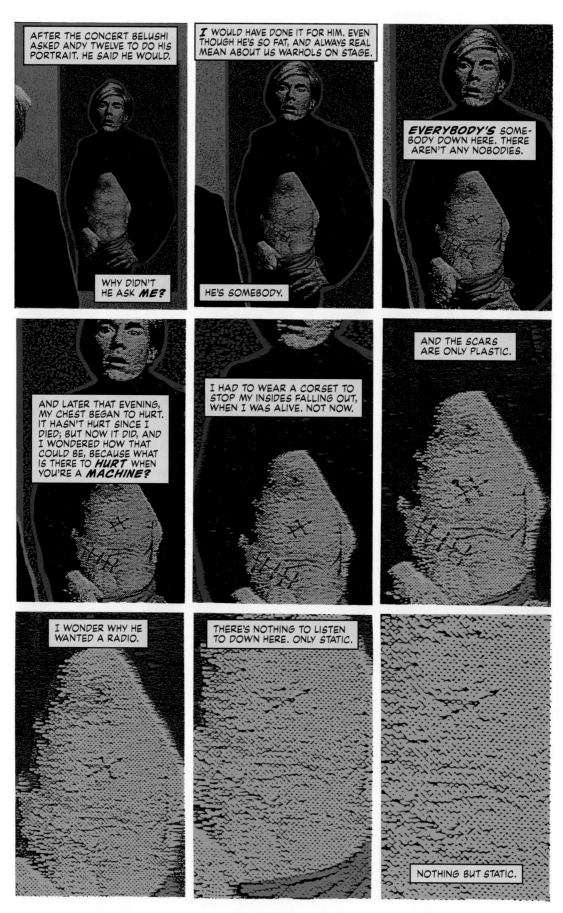

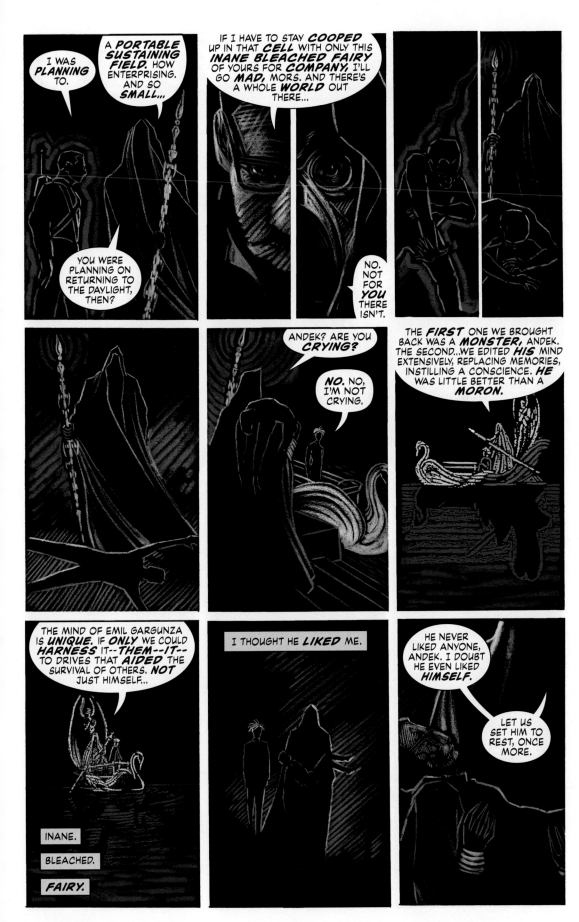

I MUST THINK ON THIS FURTHER.

EVENTUALLY, I HAVE NO DOUBT, I WILL GET THE BALANCE *RIGHT*.

THEY HUNG THERE, ON THE WALL, STARING DOWN AT ME. ROWS OF EYES, LOOKING AT ME FROM ALL THESE DEAD FACES.

IT WAS BEAUTIFUL.

I COULD HAVE SOLD IT FOR MILLIONS.

I COULD HAVE WRITTEN MY OWN CHEQUE.

THAT'S ART.

I THINK TOMORROW I'LL BUILD MY OWN.

SO HE *NEVER* LOVED ME. I NEVER *THOUGHT* HE DID. AND HE WAS SO *UGLY,* ANYWAY.

SO WHAT.

THAT'S WHAT I SAY.

SO WHAT.

OCTOBER 28TH, 1993.

SOMETIMES, I WONDER WHERE ALL THE NEW FESTIVALS CAME FROM.

THEY SEEM TO HAVE SPRUNG UP SPONTANEOUSLY, FROM GROUND LEVEL, NEITHER IMPOSED NOR EVEN SUGGESTED FROM ABOVE.

FEBRUARY THE 4TH, FOR EXAMPLE, IS REBIRTH DAY. ALL CRIMES AND DEBTS AND OFFENSES ARE FORGIVEN; THE NEW YEAR STARTS WITH A CLEAN SLATE, IN MEMORY OF THE DAY IN 1982 WHEN MICHAEL MORAN BECAME MIRACLEMAN, HIS REBIRTH PRESAGING THE WORLD'S.

LAST FEBRUARY, FOR EXAMPLE, I FORGAVE JACK FOR HAVING AN AFFAIR WITH SOME LITTLE SLUT HE'D MET ON HIS TRIP TO OSAKA.

I'VE NEVER MENTIONED IT SINCE.

FOR MY PART, I ADMITTED THAT IT WAS ME WHO SCRATCHED ONE OF HIS DUMB DIXIE CUPS SINGLES.

HELL HATH NO FURY LIKE A VINTAGE VINYL COLLECTOR, BUT HE'S NEVER SAID ANYTHING MORE ABOUT IT.

AUGUST THE 17TH IS LONDON'S DAY AND, WE MOURN THOSE TAKEN BY THE ADVERSARY.

THE MOURNING CONTINUES FOR FIVE DAYS. LAST YEAR, FOR THE FIRST TIME, I FASTED FOR THE FULL FIVE DAYS, EATING NOTHING AT ALL, DRINKING NOTHING BUT WATER. I DON'T KNOW WHAT MADE ME THINK OF FASTING, BUT IT SEEMED RIGHT.

THIS YEAR I ALSO FASTED. BUT THEN, ALMOST EVERY-ONE ELSE SEEMED TO BE FASTING TOO.

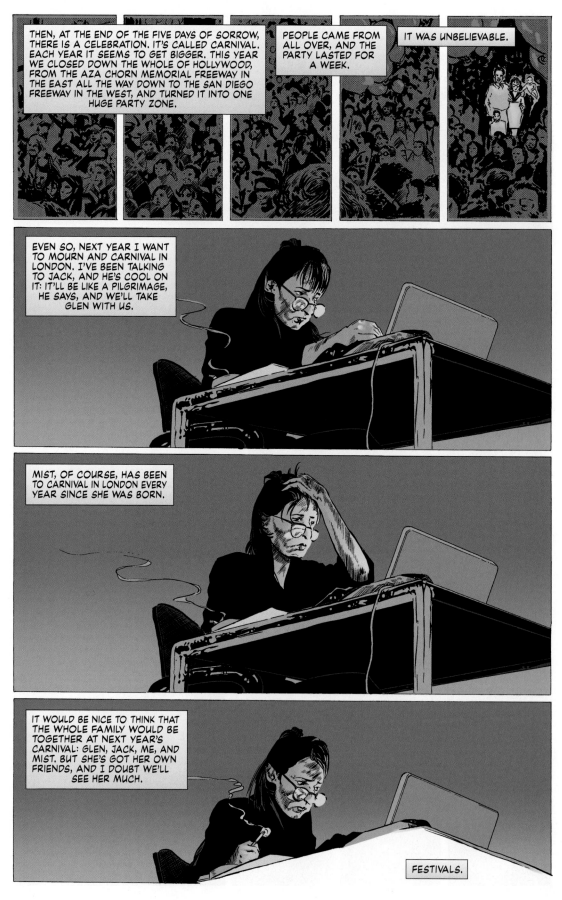

THEN, AT THE END OF THE FIVE DAYS OF SORROW, THERE IS A CELEBRATION. IT'S CALLED CARNIVAL. EACH YEAR IT SEEMS TO GET BIGGER. THIS YEAR WE CLOSED DOWN THE WHOLE OF HOLLYWOOD, FROM THE AZA CHORN MEMORIAL FREEWAY IN THE EAST ALL THE WAY DOWN TO THE SAN DIEGO FREEWAY IN THE WEST, AND TURNED IT INTO ONE HUGE PARTY ZONE.

PEOPLE CAME FROM ALL OVER, AND THE PARTY LASTED FOR A WEEK.

IT WAS UNBELIEVABLE.

EVEN SO, NEXT YEAR I WANT TO MOURN AND CARNIVAL IN LONDON. I'VE BEEN TALKING TO JACK, AND HE'S COOL ON IT: IT'LL BE LIKE A PILGRIMAGE, HE SAYS, AND WE'LL TAKE GLEN WITH US.

MIST, OF COURSE, HAS BEEN TO CARNIVAL IN LONDON EVERY YEAR SINCE SHE WAS BORN.

IT WOULD BE NICE TO THINK THAT THE WHOLE FAMILY WOULD BE TOGETHER AT NEXT YEAR'S CARNIVAL: GLEN, JACK, ME, AND MIST. BUT SHE'S GOT HER OWN FRIENDS, AND I DOUBT WE'LL SEE HER MUCH.

FESTIVALS.

THERE'S STILL NEW YEAR'S, OF COURSE, AND VALENTINE'S--AND CHRISTMAS, WHEN WE REMEMBER ALL THE DEAD GODS AND LOST MYTHOLOGIES, AND EXCHANGE PRESENTS.

GLEN STILL BELIEVES IN SANTA CLAUS.

MIST SAYS SHE LOOKED ALL OVER THE NORTH POLE, AND COULDN'T FIND HIS HOUSE, BUT GLEN SAYS SHE JUST WASN'T LOOKING IN THE RIGHT PLACES.

HE'S SO CUTE.

AND SHE'S SO...

FESTIVALS.

TOMORROW, ALL OVER THE WORLD, CHILDREN WILL WAKE UP EXCITED AND PROUD: IT'S THEIR SPECIAL DAY. ADULTS WILL STEP BACK, AND, FOR ONE DAY, EVERYTHING WILL TURN UPSIDE-DOWN AS THE CHILDREN HELP DRIVE THE TRAINS AND FIRE TRUCKS, PRESENT THE NEWS, AND RAMPAGE THROUGH THE ADULTS-ONLY SECTIONS OF THE COMMUNI-CATIONS NET. WE KEEP AN EYE ON THEM, PICK THEM UP WHEN THEY FALL OVER, AND TRY NOT TO ACT TOO OVERANXIOUS.

TOMORROW IS THEIR DAY. THEY PICKED IT, THEY CELEBRATE IT.

TOMORROW IS OCTOBER THE 29TH.

WINTERSDAY.

91

94

95

WINTER'S TALE

Written by
Neil Gaiman

Illustrated by
Mark Buckingham

Color Art by
D'Israeli

Lettered by
Todd Klein

Winter was nearly half a year old.

She wanted to go into space to find things out.

"I'm going to see the Qys," she said to her daddy. "There are lots of things they can teach me. Bye bye."

"Bye bye, Winter," said Miracleman.

She stopped off behind the moon. "Which way are the Qys?" Winter asked Aza Chorn, the Warpsmith.

He thought for a little, then he pointed. "Do you see that star?" he asked.

"Yes," said Winter, who had very good eyes.

"There," said Aza Chorn.

"Then that's the way I'm going to go," said Winter, and off she went.

"Bye bye, Winter," said Aza Chorn.

Soon the sun was just another star. Winter flew on.

The Skella Merchants in their big bone ship caught Winter in their great glass nets.

"What have we here?" they asked themselves.

"Winter," said Winter.

"We've trawled a million-million things in our travels," said the Skella Merchants. "We've trawled bottles and diamonds and quibblefrands and Anything Machines. We've trawled guns and gewgews and gilly flowers, hats and ships and asteroids. But in all the years we've been trawling, and all the things we've trawled, we've never caught a Winter in our great glass nets before."

"Well, now you have," said Winter, "so why don't you invite her in for tea?"

The Skella Merchants invited Winter in for tea.

"Where are you going?" they asked her.

"I'm going to see the Qys," she said.

"Are you going through overspace or underspace?" they asked her.

"What's the difference?" said Winter.

"Qys ships go through underspace," they said, "where they keep their bodies. It makes the journey quicker. We go through overspace, and on the way we find all manner of things that people have left behind them. It's a slow journey, but the Skella Merchants live as long as they want to, so we don't mind."

"First of all I want to go through overspace," said Winter. "I will meet more people that way."

The Skella Merchants showed Winter a little boat.

"Do you want to buy our little boat?" they asked her. "It will go even faster than you can fly: it floats on waves of light, and light pushes its sails."

"How much?" she asked.

"What do you own?" they asked her.

"Nothing," said Winter, and she smiled a big smile. "And Everything."

"Then it's yours already," said the Skella Merchants, and they showed Winter around her boat, showed her how to tack and reach and run.

Winter climbed into her little boat. "Bye bye, Skella Merchants," she said. "Thank you."

"Bye bye, Winter," said the Skella Merchants.

So Winter sailed away in her silver star boat, scudding on waves of light across the gulf.

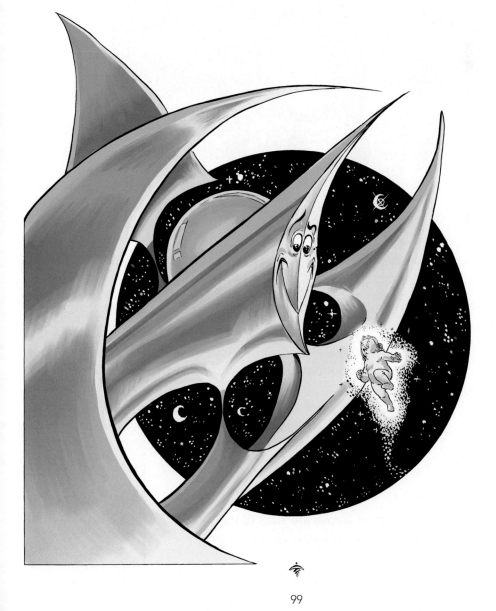

The first of the Gulf Worlds she visited was the home of the Perlii.

They welcomed Winter, but they found it strange that she was on her own.

"Where is your mate?" they asked her.

"I don't have one," said Winter.

The Perlii thought this very odd. They married just after birth, and remained together until they died.

Everywhere they went, they went together.

"You must be very lonely," they said to her.

"I'm not lonely; I'm Winter," said Winter, and she laughed her Winter's laugh and went back into the sky.

"Bye bye, Winter," said the Perlii.

I KNOW WHY THE PERLII WENT EVERYWHERE TOGETHER. WINTER TOLD ME.

IT'S BECAUSE THE FEMALES ONLY GO ON HEAT THREE TIMES IN THEIR LIVES, FOR ABOUT FIVE MINUTES A TIME, AND IF THE MALES AREN'T WITH THEM, THEN ANOTHER MALE WILL IMPREGNATE THEM...

I'M SURE THAT'S RIGHT, DEAR. NOW...

Winter sailed her little boat on across the stars of the gulf. She met lots of people. But she never stopped for very long.

One day Winter blinked.

And between the beginning of the blink and the end, a Blue Warpsmith was standing on her little boat.

"Hello, Winter," said the Blue Warpsmith. "I have a message for you from the Black Warpsmiths."

"Hello. Why are you blue?" asked Winter.

"Blue Warpsmiths are artists and dancers and painters and bureaucrats," said the Warpsmith, whose name was Lona Krill.

"White Warpsmiths are warriors. Grey Warpsmiths are diplomats. Red Warpsmiths tend the hearts of stars…"

"And Black Warpsmiths?" asked Winter.

WHAT'S A…A…BURROW-CAT?

BUREAUCRAT, GLEN. IT'S SOMEONE WHO MANIPULATES AND UTILISES INFORMATION AND CHANNELS OF COMMUNICATION. AND THEY REGULATE THINGS FROM AN OFFICIAL STANDPOINT.

IF A WARP-SMITH DIES, THE BLUE WARPSMITHS ASSIGN A NEW ONE TO TAKE THEIR PLACE.

HUH?

UM, A BUREAUCRAT IS SOMEONE WHO KNOWS LOTS OF THINGS, GLENNY.

OH.

"They are very big," said Lona Krill. "They sent me to say that The Adversary is destroying London. He and your family are going to have a fight."

"Let me know who wins," said Winter.

"I will," said Lona Krill. He went away.

Then he came back. "Your father won," said Lona Krill, "and Aza Chorn is dead."

"I thought father would win," said Winter. "Bye bye, Lona Krill."

I WANT TO SAY IT FIRST: BYE BYE, WINTER.

"Bye bye, Winter," said Lona Krill.

Winter stopped at Sauk.

"Will you marry me?" asked the Lantiman of Sauk. "You can be my newest child-bride."

"All right," said Winter. "I've never been married before." She married the Lantiman of Sauk.

He was very big, but he made Winter laugh. He gave her a world of her own, and for a present he told her the biggest secret in the universe.

But he made her promise not to tell a soul what it was.

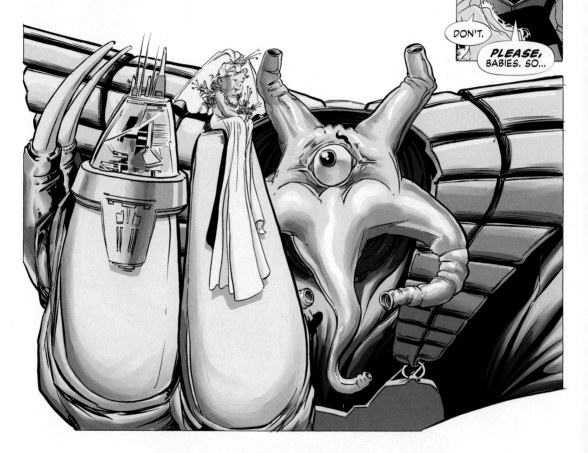

"How long will it take me to get to the Qys' star, in my little boat?" she asked him.

"Seven hundred and three thousand years, two months, and eleven minutes," said the Lantiman of Sauk.

"Then I think it's time for me to go," said Winter. She kissed the Lantiman on his big eye.

"You were the best bride I ever had," he said, sadly.

"You were the best husband I ever had," said Winter. "Bye bye, Lantiman of Sauk."

"Bye bye, Winter."

Winter had an idea. She called for a Warpsmith.

"Hello, Winter," said Kana Blur.

"Hello, Kana Blur," said Winter. "Show me your magic skin."

From before they are born, Warpsmiths have magic skin. That is how a Warpsmith warps.

Kana Blur showed Winter his magic skin.

IT'S NOT REALLY MAGIC SKIN. IT'S CALLED DERMA-CIRCUITRY. IT'S BIO-ENGINEERING, IMPLANTED FROM BIRTH. THE GULF WORLDS MADE THE BLACK WARPSMITHS, AND THE BLACK WARPSMITHS MADE ALL THE REST.

WINTER FINE-TUNED HER AURA, SO IT SERVED THE SAME FUNCTION. SO IT MIMICKED THE CIRCUITRY.

Winter made herself magic skin, just like Kana Blur's, but in her head. She made it out of her glow.

No-one had ever done this before, except a Black Warpsmith.

That was when there were four Black Warpsmiths.

Now there are only three.

Kana Blur said, "That is good magic skin, Winter."

Winter wiggled her little fingers.

And she was a long way away.

"Bye bye, Winter," said Kana Blur, to the place where Winter had been.

Winter could not warp as well as a Warpsmith. But she was the first person who was not a Warpsmith to warp anything at all.

She warped to the edge of the universe, where the Whisper slinks.

She warped to the home of the Lantiman of Sauk, but he was asleep.

She warped to London, where they were building a big house in the ruins, but no-one saw her. She was only there for a moment.

Winter warped back to her little boat.

"I thought you had left me for good," said her little boat. "I was so sad."

Winter gave her boat a big hug.

Then Winter warped her boat into the sky of the Qys world.

The Qys were very happy to see her.

Winter met the Queenking of all the Qys, who is as big as a moon. They talked for a long time.

The Queenking liked Winter very much. Then Winter went out of that place to explore the world of the Qys.

The Qys live for a very long time. They don't have children anymore. Winter was the first child on Qys in more than a million years.

They had a big party for her.

Then the Qys told Winter everything she wanted to know.

They taught Winter lots of things.

(None of them knew the secret the Lantiman of Sauk had told Winter, but now that is her secret, too, and to this day Winter has told no-one what it is.)

They showed Winter how to put her mind into other bodies.

This is Winter as a giant fish.

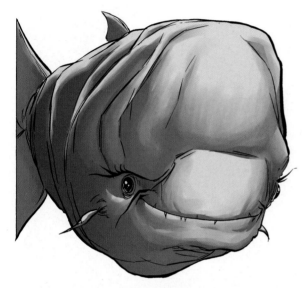

This is Winter as a Rainbow Ghost.

This is Winter as a wiggly viral coil.

This is Winter as a squishnaw-ttar.

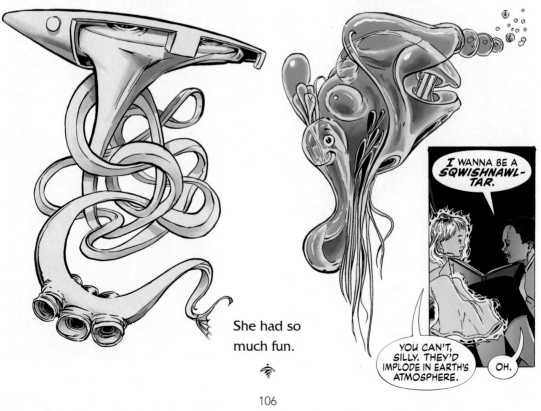

She had so much fun.

Then one day Winter said to the Qys, "It's time to go home now. I have learned a lot of things. Thank you for having me."

The Qys said, "Thank you for coming. Come back again soon."

"Perhaps I will," said Winter. "Bye bye."

"Bye bye, Winter," said the Qys.

Winter climbed into her little boat, and warped a hole into underspace.

She made a little sun, and put it behind her boat. The light from the sun pushed her little boat along.

She sailed it down the trade ways.

Far away she could see bodies stretching away into the distance, more than you could count if you started today and finished when you were a hundred and two.

She came out of underspace in a hole above Wiltshire.

Winter warped her little boat into orbit.

"Bye bye, little boat," she said.

"Bye bye, Winter," said the little boat. "Come and ride me again soon."

Winter sat in the Wiltshire snow.

She made a snowball.

She made a bigger snowball.

She put the little snowball on top of the big snowball.

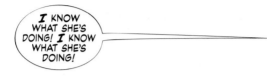

She put in a twig. She put in two pebbles.

She gave the snowman a big smile.

Then she flew to London.

At the top of the biggest house in the whole wide world, she sat and she waited.

When he came home, her daddy got a big surprise. Here was his little girl. She wasn't a baby any more.

"Hello, Winter," said Miracleman.

Winter grinned.

"I'm back," she said.

THE END

110

I WANTED SOMEONE WHO WAS SPECIAL TO ME.

SOMEONE WHO'D NEVER LEAVE ME. OR NOT FOR A LONG TIME...

MAYBE TOMORROW.

MAYBE TOMORROW SHE'LL WAKE UP AND REALISE SHE NEEDS ME.

AND MAYBE THE SKELLA MERCHANTS WILL GIVE US A LITTLE SILVER SKY BOAT, AND TOGETHER WE'LL SAIL AWAY INTO THE STARS, TOGETHER, AND NEVER COME BACK.

AND MAYBE...

HERE IT COMES. *I* DUNNO. BUSSES, *EH?* YOU WAIT AROUND FOR HALF AN HOUR, AND THEN *THREE* COME *TOGETHER.*

I SHRUG.

NORTH-WEST

CITY TRANSPORT

OBVIOUSLY NOT THE RIGHT RESPONSE.

I STARE AT HIM HELPLESSLY. IS THAT A SIGNIFICANT PHRASE? SHOULD I BE COMING BACK WITH A COUNTERSIGN? OR IS HE SIMPLY MAKING CONVERSATION?

THE *PLUMBER* STILL DIDN'T COME, I SEE.

I MEAN, WHAT'S THE POINT? IT'LL BE OUT ON VIDEO EVENTUALLY.

RODNEY, DON'T *DO* THAT. EVERYBODY'S LOOKING.

SO *HE* SAYS, IF YOU'RE COMING HOME LOOKING LIKE THAT, YOUNG LADY, *YOU'VE* GOT ANOTHER THINK COMING. WELL, *I* SAID TO *HIM, I* SAID...

WEST CITY EYES ONLY

PROJECT CINDERELLA

IT'S THE *RUSSIANS.* IT'S THE *GERMANS.* IT'S THE *CHINESE.* IT'S THE *AMERICANS.* IT'S THE *GODS.* IT'S THE BLOODY *GODS.*

OH-OH. A LOONY.

HULLO, LADY.

THERE'S PEOPLE FROM VENUS BEAMING SEXY PICTURES INTO MY MIND.

I DON'T SLEEP ANYMORE. NOBODY WILL SPY FOR ME. PEOPLE UPSTAIRS DANCE ALL NIGHT. *WHERE* ARE THE SNOWS OF BLOODY *YESTERYEAR,* EH?

I'M SORRY. EXCUSE ME. THIS IS MY STOP.

NO PROBLEM, LADY. *GOD* LOVES YOU. IT'S *ME* HE BLOODY LOATHES.

I HATE LOONIES.

WHEN I WAS IN WASHINGTON, BALLARD WENT CRAZY. JUST CRACKED COMPLETELY. ALDERMAN AND I HAD TO ENSURE HIS SILENCE-- SNEAK HIM FROM SAFE HOUSE TO SAFE HOUSE, DRUGGED UP TO THE EYEBALLS, UNTIL WE COULD GET HIM BACK TO THE U.K.

FISHMONG

TURNED OUT LATER HE WAS WORKING FOR MOSSAD, AND THE INTEL SECTOR OF A JAPANESE CONGLOMERATE, AND ALSO REPORTING BACK TO WASHINGTON.

MUST HAVE BEEN THE PRESSURE OF KEEPING ALL THE BALLS IN THE AIR THAT FINALLY PUSHED HIM OUT OF HIS TREE.

YOU'RE A SIGHT FOR SORE EYES, MISS. WHAT CAN I DO FOR YOU TODAY?

SIGN: I'M LOOKING FOR A NICE PIECE OF HAKE.

SORRY, LOVE. WE'RE ALL OUT OF HAKE. I CAN DO YOU SOME LOVELY MACKEREL.

COUNTERSIGN.

FINAL RESPONSE: I FANCIED SOMETHING LESS OILY.

AH. I SEE. WELL, STEP BACK HERE, AND LET'S SEE WHAT WE CAN FIND...

DOWN A CORRIDOR, SMELLING OF FISH; INTO A SMALL SITTING ROOM. THE BLINDS ARE DRAWN, AND THE NYMAN SOUNDTRACK TO "THE DRAUGHTSMAN'S CONTRACT" PLAYS SOFTLY IN THE BACKGROUND.

TUESDAY.

ON THE WAY TO WORK, I SEE McALLISTER: HE'S SELLING PAPERS ON THE STREET CORNER. HE USED TO BE MY HEAD OF OPS IN BEIRUT. THAT WAS A LONG TIME AGO, IN A DIFFERENT CITY.

NORTHWEST CITY GAZETTE

SOUTH EASTERN CITY MAYOR RESIGNS

I BUY A PAPER FROM HIM; I OWE HIM THAT MUCH.

DON'T FORGET YOUR CHANGE, LOVE.

NORTHWEST CITY GAZETTE   Classified Advertis

FUNNY, RUNNING INTO HIM HERE. HE DOESN'T APPEAR TO RECOGNISE ME.

SOUTH CITY

USUAL DULL NEWS OF THE CITY. NOTHING MUCH EVER HAPPENS HERE. NOTHING EVER CHANGES. IT'S TUESDAY, SO I TURN TO PAGE 25.

WEAR A HAPPY FACE IN THE CITY

IT'S THERE, HIDDEN IN THE SMALL ADS. NOT A COMPLEX CIPHER-- JUST A SET OF CODE PHRASES TO INDICATE A MEETING POINT, A DROP, OR A PHONE NUMBER.

LAZILY, I SCAN THE OTHER ADS.

DO THEY ALSO HIDE MESSAGES? "CHILD'S BLUE PUSHCHAIR FOR SALE. C$12.50 OR NEAREST OFFER." DOES THAT SIGNAL A BREAK-IN? A TREACHERY? A BETRAYAL?

IN TO WORK. MY COVER'S NOT A BAD ONE: I'M A SURVEYOR, ABLE TO WALK THE CITY AS I NEED.

CITY SURVEYORS

THE CITY. LOVE IT.

THERE'S NO REASON FOR ME TO FEEL SO BAD. BUT I DO.

MAYBE I'M CRACKING UP: I'VE BEEN IN THE FIELD TOO LONG. I WISH I COULD GET A RECALL HOME.

...WHERE IS HOME, ANYWAY?

HOWARD?

SHIT! RUTH, HOW THE **HELL** DID YOU GET IN HERE?

TRAINED FOR A **LONG** TIME, HOWIE. NOW, I WAN' YOU TO TELL ME SOMETHING.

LOOK, I **KNOW** YOU'RE UNDER **STRESS.** WHY DON'T YOU...

SHUT UP, HOWARD. ARE YOU A SPY?

HUH? RUTH, ARE YOU **CRAZY?**

I JUST WANT AN ANSWER. **YES** OR **NO.**

AND IF IT'S THE WRONG ANSWER, I'LL SLIT YOUR FUCKING THROAT.

SO: ARE YOU A SPY?

UHN... NO...I...

I'M A SPY, HOWARD. NOW, HOW ABOUT **YOU?** I'LL COUNT TO THREE.

ONE...

TWO...

I KEEP RUNNING THROUGH THE SHADOWS.

IN THE OLD DAYS SOMETHING LIKE THIS WOULD HAVE THE ADRENALINE FLOODING THROUGH MY BODY. NOT NOW. I JUST RUN, FEELING FAINTLY SICK.

CITY POLICE

NEARLY THERE.

I'VE GONE AS FAR AS I CAN GO.

I'M ON THE EDGE OF THE CITY. BUT UNTIL TODAY I DON'T THINK IT HAD OCCURRED TO ME THERE WAS AN EDGE TO THE CITY.

DANGER

PRETTY SOON, THEY'LL COME TO TAKE ME BACK. THEY'LL TAKE THE KNOWLEDGE OUT OF MY HEAD AND SET ME TO SPYING ONCE MORE. BUT RIGHT NOW, I'M SANE AND SAFE INSIDE MY HEAD...

133

I WAS GIVEN THE CHOICE OF LIVING ANYWHERE ON EARTH I WISHED.

I CHOSE BRISTOL, IN THE ENGLISH SOUTHWEST. I WAS BORN HERE AND THE CITY HELD PLEASANT MEMORIES FOR ME. IT HAS CHANGED, THOUGH, IN THIS NEW AGE.

IT'S CLEANER AND THE PEOPLE ARE HAPPIER, LESS RUSHED, MORE PEACEFUL.

BUT...

I'M WORKING AS A LIBRARIAN. IT'S A REWARDING PROFESSION, OBTAINING INFORMATION FOR PEOPLE, LEADING THEM TO THE FICTIONS THEY NEED.

EVEN SO...

I'VE BEGUN A RELATION-SHIP. HER NAME IS IDA, AND WE HAVE NO SECRETS.

I TOLD HER THE STORY OF MY PAST. SHE FINDS IT INTEREST-ING, BUT NOTHING MORE.

IT'S THE FIRST TIME I'VE EVER BEEN COMFORTABLE SPENDING THE NIGHT WITH ANOTHER...

...UNWORRIED ABOUT ANY SECRETS I MIGHT BLURT OUT IN MY SLEEP.

BUT STILL...

I WATCH THE PEOPLE.

SOMETIMES I FIND MYSELF LISTENING TO THEIR CONVER-SATIONS, WONDERING IF THEY ARE TALKING IN OBLIQUE SIGN AND COUNTERSIGN.

...AND THEN THREE COME ALONG TOGETHER.

I BUY MY FISH FROM THE FISH-MONGER AND WONDER IF HIS PROFESSION IS SIMPLY A FLAW-LESSLY MAINTAINED COVER.

THE COMPUTER NETS GIVE OPEN INFORMATION ON ANYTHING I CAN IMAGINE. AND STILL I WONDER WHAT SECRETS ARE HIDDEN THERE.

THIS MORNING, I CAUGHT MYSELF NOT GETTING IN THE FIRST TAXI THAT CAME ALONG.

PERHAPS TOMORROW I WILL WAKE BACK IN THE CITY ONCE MORE, BACK IN THE WILD WORLD OF MIRRORS AND NUMBERS AND LIES.

BRISTOL HACKNEY CABS: NO. 1860

TAXI

BUT THAT ISN'T WHAT SCARES ME.

WHAT SCARES ME IS THIS:

IT'S NOT THE WORLD I REMEMBER. MAYBE AT THE EDGE OF THIS WORLD THERE'S A WALL, AND BEYOND IT'S ANOTHER WORLD--EVEN BIGGER AND MORE REAL.

. 1860

AND ONE DAY I'LL HAVE TO GO OVER THE WALL.

AND THEY'RE WATCHING ME.

AUGUST 22ND, 1994.

5:30 P.M.

I SPOKE TO A FRIEND OF MINE LAST MONTH ABOUT HAPPY ENDINGS. SHE WAS WRITING A BOOK, AND WANTED TO KNOW WHAT THE HAPPIEST ENDING I COULD THINK OF WAS.

BALLOONS, I TOLD HER.

A BIG PARTY, WITH BALLOONS.

ANITA AND I ARRIVED IN LONDON THIS MORNING. WE SPENT THE MORNING WALKING THE WEST BASE OF OLYMPUS, GAPING LIKE RUBES.

MIRACLE WOMAN ~

w a r h o l

MIRACLE WOMAN

WE TRIED TO IDENTIFY THE STATUARY--THE CLASSICAL MASTERPIECES TAKEN FROM GALLERIES, THE REPRO-DUCTIONS, THE ORIGINALS CREATED FOR THE PYRAMID BY ARTISTS.

SHE WAS FAR MORE SUCCESSFUL THAN I WAS. "*YOU'VE* GOT THE FINE ART DEGREE," SHE POINTED OUT, AFTER I HAD FAILED TO IDENTIFY CELLINI'S *PERSEUS AND MEDUSA.*

"BUT *YOU'VE* GOT THE GUIDEBOOK," I TOLD HER. "ANYWAY, THAT WAS *THEN*. NOW I'M JUST A HUMBLE WIND-MILLER."

Street Atlas and Ind

A-Z

Geographers' A-Z Map Comp

Wall's ICE CREAM

I BOUGHT TWO ICE CREAMS, ONE WITH CHOCOLATE FLAKE IN, ONE WITHOUT.

I ♥ MM

WE ATE THEM IN SILENCE, STARING UPWARDS.

LONDON.

THERE'S A PRE-CARNIVAL AFTERNOON TENSION IN THE AIR THAT I RECOGNISE FROM LOS ANGELES: THE TRUE MOURNING IS OVER, THE CELEBRATION HAS NOT YET BEGUN.

I SPENT THE FULL FIVE DAYS OF MOURNING IN THE KILLING FIELDS.

I WANDERED WITHOUT EATING, DRINKING ONLY WATER FROM THE CANISTERS ON MY BACK.

I DID NOT WASH.

I SLEPT ON A BED OF ASHES OR ON GRASS, WHEREVER I FOUND MYSELF AT NIGHTFALL, AND DREAMED DARK DREAMS OF THE DEAD.

IT WAS HOT, DURING THE DAYS.

FROM TIME TO TIME I WOULD SEE ANOTHER MOURNER. EVEN WHEN OUR PATHS CROSSED, WE WOULD NOT TALK.

AFTER A WHILE I BEGAN TO HALLUCINATE: THE STARK, NOUMINOUS HALLUCINATION OF A PROPHET IN A DESERT, AND IT SEEMED THE BONES WERE TALKING TO ME.

I REMEMBER SITTING AND HOLDING A CONVERSATION WITH A MUMMIFIED WOMAN, HER EYES STILL OPEN IN HEAT-FLASHED TERROR.

"HE *BURNED* ME WITH HIS *EYES,*" SHE KEPT SAYING. "THE *DRAGON* CAME AND HE *BURNED* ME WITH HIS EYES."

137

I ASK IDA AGAIN WHY WE CAN'T CARNIVAL IN BRISTOL. SHE TELLS ME, AND I DON'T HEAR HER BECAUSE A SIX-FOOT-TWO NAKED BLACK WOMAN WITH A PENIS, WEARING A LEOPARD-SKIN CAPE AND NOTHING ELSE, HAS JUST WALKED PAST.

IDA TELLS ME IT'S RUDE TO STARE.

I SAY, SURE, BUT I MEAN, DID YOU *SEE* THAT? I MEAN, DID YOU SEE *HER*? SHE WAS...SHE WAS...*BEAUTIFUL!*

IDA JUST GRINS.

"THAT'S WHY WE AREN'T CARNIVALLING IN BRISTOL," SAYS IDA.

140

IT'S STRANGE. WHEN I USED TO PLAN THIS TRIP IT WAS ALWAYS AS A FAMILY.

ME, JACK, GLEN, EVEN MIST.

BUT NO.

IT'S JUST ME.

THE MOURNING CAME EASY.

IT'S THE CELEBRATION I'M SCARED OF.

SHARON. *LOOK.* THOSE T-SHIRTS. THEY'RE *WONDERFUL.*

YOU LIKE THEM?

YEAH. THEY'RE REALLY *CRUEL.*

I AM HONOURED BY YOUR ADMIRATION. WHICH IS YOUR FAVOURITE?

THE BABY BATES ONE. IT'S *TRIFFIC.*

HERE. IT'S *YOURS.*

THANK YOU. I'M HONOURED.

UH, IN APPRECIATION OF YOUR GIFT, PLEASE, LET ME *ALSO* GIVE YOU SOMETHING.

HERE.

IT'S LOVELY. I *ALSO* AM HONOURED.

YOU GOT ANY *STRING?*

STRING? OH. YEAH. SOMEWHERE. HANG ON.

HOW DO I LOOK?

HOW DO YOU *LOOK?*

YOU LOOK *FINE,* JACKS. STOP SHOWIN' OFF. COME ON.

ON THE LAST DAY OF MY FAST, EVERY-
THING BEGAN TO COME INTO FOCUS.
THE HALLUCINATIONS STOPPED. EVERY-
THING HAD A HEIGHTENED CLARITY: IT
SEEMED MORE REAL THAN ANYTHING I
HAD BELIEVED POSSIBLE. REAL COLOURS.
REAL TEXTURES. REAL SOUNDS.

AND THEN THE PEOPLE STARTED COMING,
IN ONES AND TWOS, HUNDREDS OF THEM,
THOUSANDS OF THEM.

THEY CARRIED FLOWERS. AND
THEY WALKED ACROSS THE
KILLING FIELDS, PICKING THEIR
WAY THROUGH THE MAZE OF
DEAD CARS AND CRACKED
MASONRY, LOOKING FOR
SPECIFIC BONES.

AND WHEN THEY FOUND THE BONES THEY WERE
LOOKING FOR, THEY'D PUT FLOWERS ON THEM.

AN IMAGE ENGRAVED
ITSELF ON MY RETINAE:
A CHILD'S SKULL, WITH
A ROSE IN IT, THREADED
CAREFULLY THROUGH
THE EYE SOCKETS.

I WANTED TO ASK THEM WHO THE
BONES HAD BELONGED TO, HOW
THEY HAD DIED, BUT I DIDN'T DARE.

I FOLLOWED THEM AT A DISTANCE,
A TRESPASSER ON PRIVATE GRIEF.

I SAT IN THE BONE
GARDEN IN THE
SHADOW OF OLYMPUS
AND BEGAN TO CRY.

IDA TUGS MY ARM, POINTS TO A POLICEMAN.

"SO? IT'S A COP." I CAN'T SEE WHY THIS IS IMPORTANT.

BUT THERE AREN'T ANY COPS. NOT ANYMORE.

WE GO OVER AND TALK TO HIM; HE'S PART OF AN HISTORICAL REENACTMENT SOCIETY. THEY GET TOGETHER ONCE A WEEK AND WEAR UNIFORMS.

THEY'VE APPOINTED THEMSELVES UNOFFICIAL MARSHALS OF THE CARNIVAL, GIVING STRANGERS DIRECTIONS, TELLING THE TIME.

I PUT ON HIS HAT.

IDA TAKES OUR PHOTO-GRAPH TOGETHER.

BUS STOP

ANITA?

MM-HMM.

CHECK THEM OUT. SPOOKY LITTLE BUGGERS, AREN'T THEY?

YEAH.

DO THEY... I MEAN. THERE WON'T BE ANY TROUBLE, WILL THERE?

NO. NO TROUBLE.

143

WHEN THE MUSIC BEGAN, I LEFT THE PLACE OF DEATH AND TOOK THE SLIDEWALK INTO NOTTING HILL. HIGHLIGHTS OF THE CARNIVAL WERE ALREADY RUNNING ON THE BILLBOARDS...

...AND THEN, ON THE EDGE OF THE CARNIVAL ZONE, THE SLIDEWAY STOPPED, AND I BEGAN TO WALK.

I WAS EDGING THROUGH THE CROWD WHEN I SAW THEM, FAR ABOVE, SPARKLING AND GLITTERING LIKE...

...LIKE CHILDREN.

IS *SHE* ONE OF THEM? I SQUINT AT THE SKY, BUT CANNOT TELL.

I KNOW SHE'LL BE HERE SOMEWHERE.

MIST.

ANITA! LOOK AT **THIS!**

WHAT IS IT?

IT'S ONE OF THOSE ENHANCED ANIMALS.

DOES IT **TALK?**

MAYBE YOU OUGHT TO ASK **HER.**

UM. HELLO. MY NAME'S JOHN GALLAWAY.

BROCK.

SO, UM, WHAT DO YOU THINK OF CARNIVAL?

IS GOOD. IS GOOD.

STILL **SMELLS** LIKE A BADGER, THOUGH.

YOU...YOU'RE **BEAUTIFUL.**

BROCK. IS BEAUTIFUL.

IT'S A SPACE-MAN!

HEY! LET HER THROUGH! IT'S A REAL SPACEMAN!

A SPACE-MAN! HERE? C'MON. QUICK.

WHAT'S A SPACEMAN?

WELL, THEY'RE SORT OF PSYCHO-PHARMACEUTICAL ASTRONAUTS. THERE AREN'T A LOT OF THEM LEFT...

THERE WERE A LOT OF THEM TO BEGIN WITH, BUT THEY HAVE A SORT OF HIGH MORTALITY RATE.

IT'S A REALLY GOOD THING TO SEE ONE. IT'S MEANT TO BE LUCKY. THEY CAN TELL YOU THINGS.

WHAT THINGS?

WELL...THINGS. PEOPLE SAY THEY CAN TELL YOU HIDDEN THINGS. PREDICT THINGS, MAYBE.

YOU MEAN LIKE THE DELPHIC ORACLE?

SOMETIMES MORE LIKE A DELPHIC FORTUNE COOKIE. YOU'LL SEE...

I HAVE A QUESTION. MY DAUGHTER. SHE'S DEAD. I WANT TO KNOW-- WHAT HAPPENS WHEN YOU DIE?

WE ARE FAR MORE FAIR SWEET SUN, FROM THE SHORES OF MY LOVE, AND IT PEELED OUT AND I MIGHT TOUCH THAT. EVERYONE'S ALL ENVOYS FROM THE FUTURE TOO. OLD FRIENDS.

WHAT DO YOU MEAN?

HOPE.

WHAT YOU DREAMED. IF THEY ASKED. YOU STILL GROOVE WITH GRIEF...

OH.

IT.

ACTUALLY THAT, DID IT IS THE FEELING THAT THERE, I DON'T LOOK FOR SENSE IN HEAVEN, I DON'T REMEMBER WHAT THE FUCK WAS GOING ON.

AYE ME.

I COULD FEEL HOW SHE SPEAKS.

WHAT DO? THAT MY JOKE: THE *HEAVEN.* I'LL LOOK INTO THE DUST FOR QUESTIONS FOREVER.

YOU DIDN'T ASK THE KIDDIN' SPACEMAN ANYTHIN', THEN?

NO *FEAR.* I MEAN, WHAT IS THERE TO *ASK?* HOW *CLOSE* AM I TO THE *TOP* OF THE *LIST?* HOW LONG AM I GOING TO HAVE TO *WAIT* UNTIL I GET A NEW BODY?

MY *SISTER* GOT AN ORACLE FROM A SPACEMAN THAT SHE SAID WAS *VITAL,* MAN, WHEN THEY WAS DEVELOPIN' THE *FLU* CURE...

YEAH? WELL, SHE'S *SMARTER* THAN MOST OF US. SO, HOW ARE WE *DOING?*

LESSEE... AN ENAMEL BOX, A PAINTING, TWO APPLES, A CAKE, A POLISHED CAPYBARA'S SKULL, THREE T-SHIRTS, A LITTLE CHINA FROG, A MIRACLEMAN COMIC AND TWO VIDEOS-- "PASS-PORT TO PIMLICO," AND SOME REALLY *WEIRD* FIFTIES CHINESE PORNO THING.

OH, AND CHECK *THIS* OUT. A SIGNED PHOTOGRAPH OF *MADONNA.*

SHE WAS HERE?

YEAH, WHILE YOU WERE OFF HAVING A SLASH. SHE TOOK ONE OF THE *DICKY DAUNTLESS* SHIRTS.

HMPH. I'M *JEALOUS.*

SHE WAS *NICE.* I DIDN'T RECOGNISE THE GUY SHE WAS WITH, THOUGH.

LISTEN, MAN, *YOU'VE* MET KIDDIN' *GOD.*

YES, YES I HAVE. HAVEN'T I?

I WATCH IN AWE.

WE'RE IN A NEW AGE, NOW.
THE WORLD BEGAN IN BLOOD
AND FIRE NINE YEARS AGO,
AND THE AGE OF MIRACLES
WAS BORN.

I REALISE, ASTONISHED, THAT
MY MOURNING FOR HOPE HAS
FINALLY ENDED. IT HAS TRANS-
MUTED INTO REGRET THAT SHE
CANNOT BE HERE WITH ME.

THE WORLD WAS REFINED IN THAT
DARK CRUCIBLE. AND THE LEADEN
AGE THROUGH WHICH WE FALTERED
HAS, BY SOME RARE ALCHEMY, BEEN
CHANGED THROUGH FLAME TO GOLD.

I WONDER HOW HE DOES WHAT HE DOES. PERHAPS HE IS SELECTIVELY IGNITING AIR MOLECULES. PERHAPS...

I'LL ASK ON THE 'NET WHEN I GET HOME TONIGHT.

IF I REMEMBER.

I LOSE TRACK OF TIME IN THE CORUSCATING SPARKS AND LIGHT AND MULTI-COLOURED FLAMES.

IT GOES ON FOREVER; AND THEN IT ENDS.

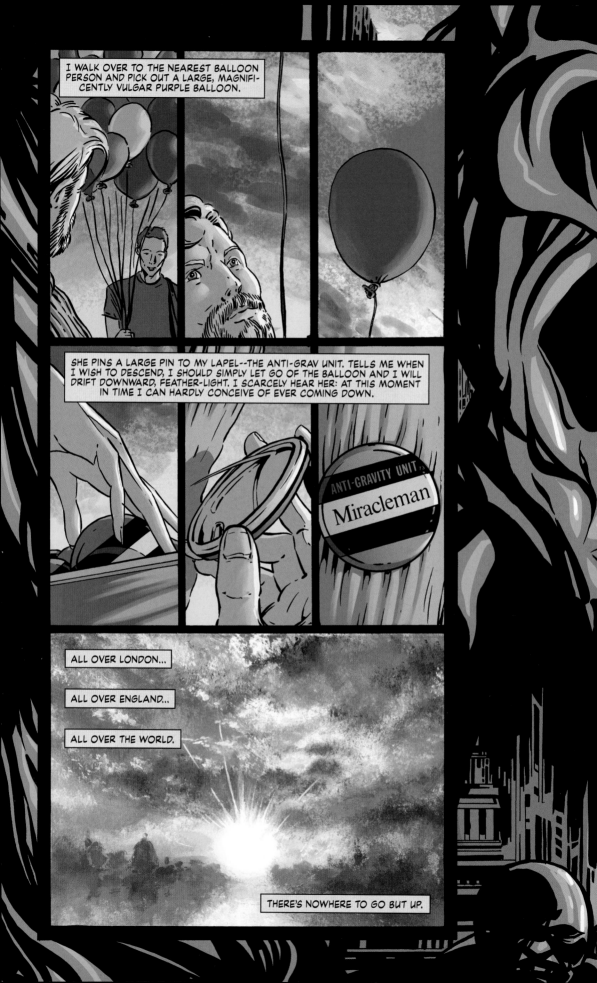

I WALK OVER TO THE NEAREST BALLOON PERSON AND PICK OUT A LARGE, MAGNIFICENTLY VULGAR PURPLE BALLOON.

SHE PINS A LARGE PIN TO MY LAPEL--THE ANTI-GRAV UNIT. TELLS ME WHEN I WISH TO DESCEND, I SHOULD SIMPLY LET GO OF THE BALLOON AND I WILL DRIFT DOWNWARD, FEATHER-LIGHT. I SCARCELY HEAR HER: AT THIS MOMENT IN TIME I CAN HARDLY CONCEIVE OF EVER COMING DOWN.

ANTI-GRAVITY UNIT

Miracleman

ALL OVER LONDON...

ALL OVER ENGLAND...

ALL OVER THE WORLD.

THERE'S NOWHERE TO GO BUT UP.

I WATCH THE SUN SETTING IN SLOW FLAME, PAINTING THE LOW SUMMER CLOUDS WITH LIGHT.

I WATCH IT; A HUGE ORANGE BALLOON THAT SEEMS TO FILL HALF THE SKY. IT COMMENCES TO SINK BELOW THE HORIZON; AND AS IT DOES, ITS LAST RAYS CATCH THE STRAY CLOUDS, SILVER AND MAUVE AND GREY; TRANSMUTE THEM TO RUBY AND AMETHYST AND GOLD.

PUREST, MOST PERFECT, ETERNAL GOLD.

CARNIVAL

Neil Gaiman's planning overview for *The Golden Age*, *The Silver Age* and *The Dark Age*, circa 1989-90.

MIRACLEMAN: Future Plans.

Neil Gaiman.

Overall, my plans for the series split up into three books, each book consisting of about six episodes. These are:

THE GOLDEN AGE --

A series of short stories, essentially optimistic, dealing with what it's like for people living in Utopia, in the late 80s and early 90s of Miracleman's world. It's the Era of the Gods.

THE SILVER AGE --

The Era of the Children of God. Round about the turn of the century -- A new Age of Man. Most of the story is ███████████
██

THE DARK AGE

Things go bad.

....

BOOK 4 The Golden Age

is divided roughly as follows.

17) Intro; Climbing Story; Retrieval (2 pages)

18) Windmill story, about a man who has an affair with Miraclewoman; Urban Legends story, of the Bates kids swapping updated greek myths; Retrieval (2 pages)

19) Miracleman in Shea Stadium; Gargunza Story "Proserpine"; Retrieval (2 pages)

20) Winter's Tale. Retrieval (2 pages)

21) Milton Keynes/The Prisoner/Spy story; Retrieval (2 pages)

22) Carnival. Retrieval (4 pages)

Of this, so far all of 17) is written, and all of Retrieval.

In early 1989 as Neil Gaiman and Mark Buckingham began their *Miracleman* story planning, Buckingham began a series of character studies to shape his approach toward the main cast. **BELOW:** Miracleman study, watercolors on hot-press watercolor paper. **INSET:** Miracleman eye study, acrylic on sketchbook paper.

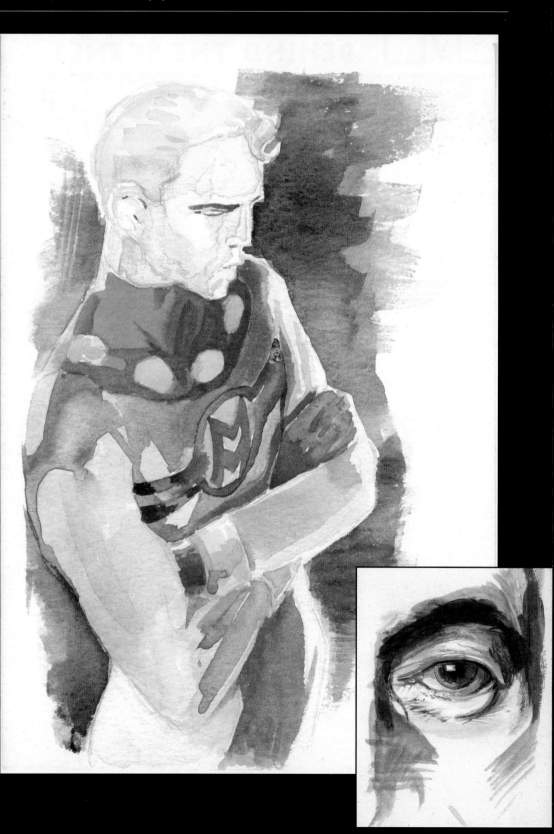

Miracleman
studies, pastel
on cold-press
watercolor paper;
the bottom
piece would
form the basis
of Buckingham's
1990 United
Kingdom Comic
Art Convention
pinup.

Some of Buckingham's exploratory sketches and concepts were abandoned, but they later ended up influencing the design of *The Golden Age*'s cast. This take on an older Winter inspired Mist's appearance in "Winter's Tale;" pencil, India ink and Letratone on sketchbook paper.

LEFT: This early doodle helped establish the look for Mist's mother, Rachel Cohn, pencil and India ink on sketchbook paper. **RIGHT:** Miraclebaby sketch, pastel on sketchbook paper.

Before finalising the art style for "A Prayer and Hope…," Buckingham created these studies of the receptionist, the environment helmets and Miracleman; pencil, India ink and Letratone on illustration board.

While Gaiman worked on the script for "Notes from the Underground," Buckingham began testing techniques for the artwork. A method utilising white pencil crayon on black cartridge proved successful, as seen in these studies. The Gargunza pieces became final art for page 4 of the story.

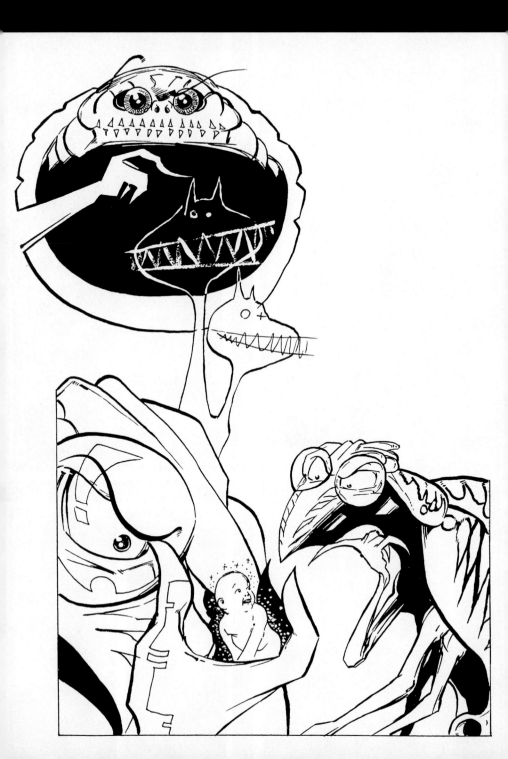

Preliminary sketches for the storybook section of "Winter's Tale," pencil and India ink on illustration board. The character at the top-left is Buckingham's storybook take on the Qys attack body from *Olympus* Chapter 1. The bottom-right figure is the Qys flying body from *Olympus* Chapter 2.

Mark Buckingham created these early tests for the paranoid characters of "Spy Story" before striking upon the final photoreference/photocopy art style; pencil, India ink, marker and Letratone on illustration board.

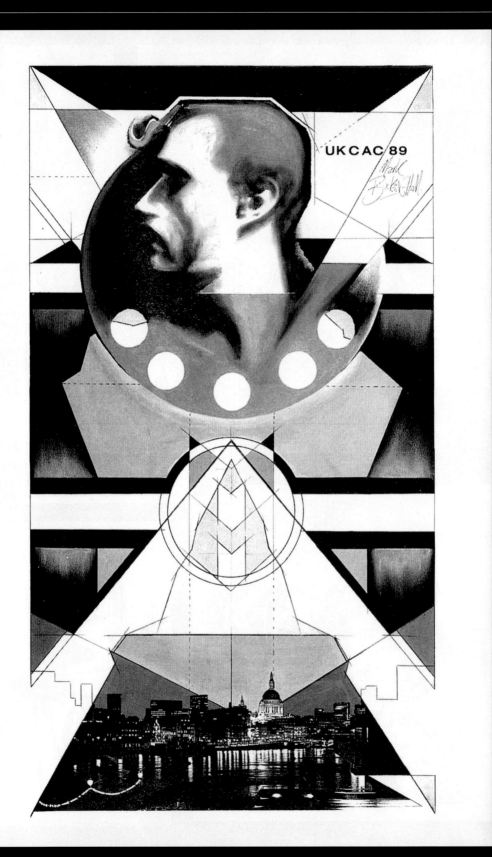

Best Wishes
to Everyone at
UKCAC 90
from
Mark
Buckingham.

BEST WiSHES
TO
EvErY○Ne
AT
UKCAC 91

from

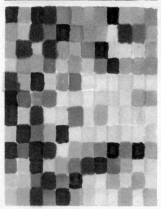

BUCkINGHAM

Greg, This is a very "rough" rough, for the Miracleman Poster.

A golden carving of M.M. along lines of convention illo.

clockwork cogs and wheels.

wires, resistors etc.

these five rings will contain mini profiles of Miraclewoman, Huey Moon, British Bulldog, The God of the Dead and Phon Moods.

shelves will be better arranged than this - but will follow forms in top half of poster.

Shelves inside the pyramid shape contain elements relating to the short stories which make up the Golden Age!

Miracleman full figure shot.

MARK BUCKINGHAM 1990

Miracleman: The Golden Age promotional coin, given out at the 1990 San Diego Comic-Con and later used as retailer incentives. The coin can also be seen as part of Mark Buckingham's 1990 *Miracleman* poster. Shown here at three times the original 1 1/8" size.

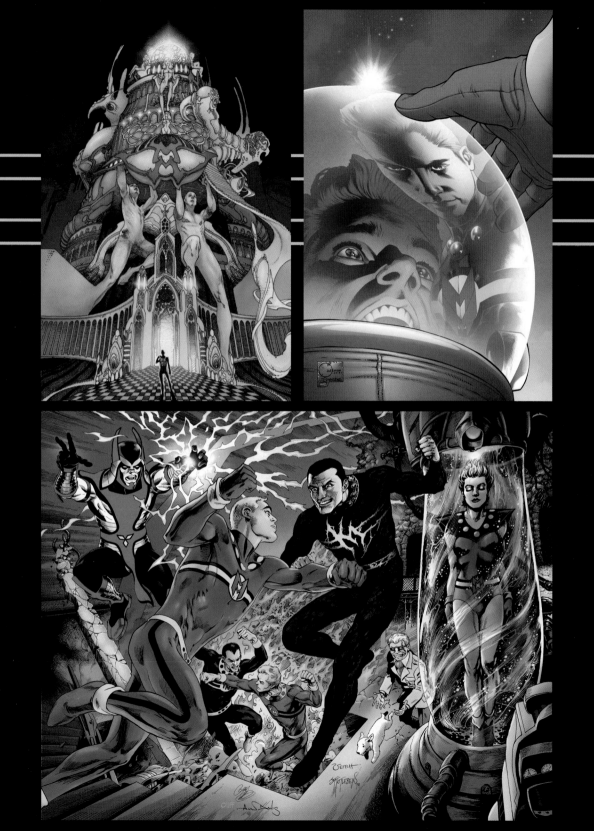

Miracleman by Gaiman & Buckingham #3 (2015) variant cover art by Mike & Laura Allred (top) and Tony Harris (bottom).

Miracleman by Gaiman & Buckingham #4 (2015) variant cover art by Charles Paul Wilson III (top) and Chris Samnee & Matt Wilson (bottom).

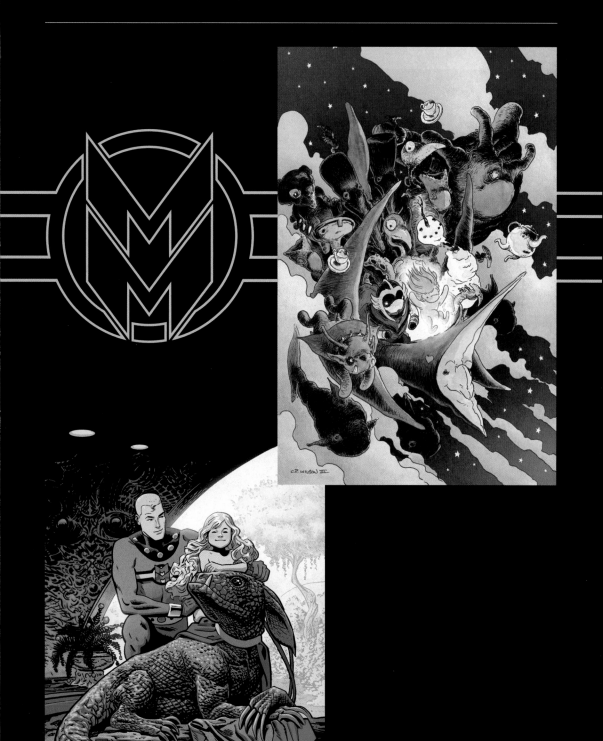

Miracleman by Gaiman & Buckingham #6 (2015) variant cover art by Kaare Andrews (top) and Olivier Coipel & Laura Martin (bottom).

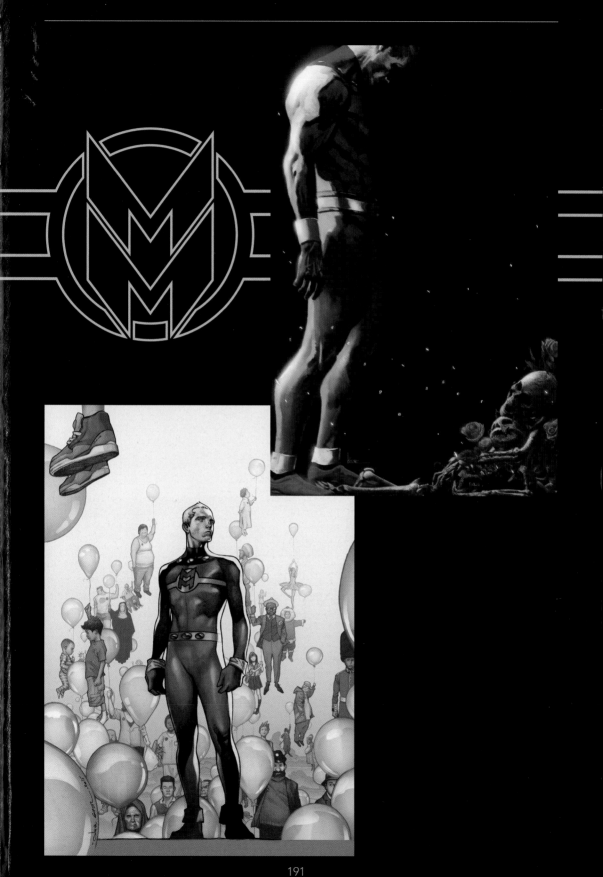

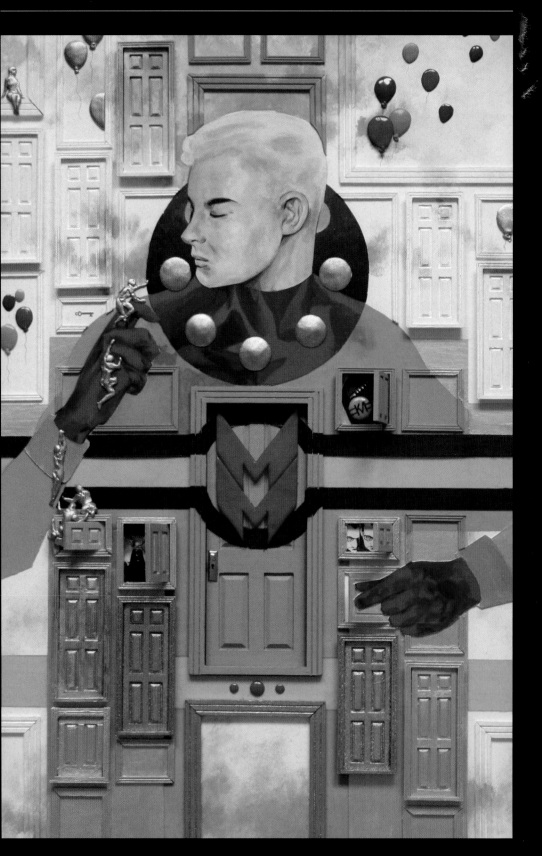